Student Workbook
Level

A Reason For Spelling® Student Workbook - Level C
Copyright ©1999 by The Concerned Group, Inc.

ISBN#0-936785-29-2

Created by MOE Studio, Inc.

Authors: Rebecca Burton, Eva Hill, Leah Knowlton, Kay Sutherland
Black and White Illustrations: James McCullough
Colorization: Mark Decker • Design and Layout: Greg Hauth
Project Leaders: Greg Sutherland, Eva Hill

Published by Concerned Communications
Post Office Box 1000, 700 East Granite, Siloam Springs, Arkansas 72761

Publisher: Russ L. Potter, II • Senior Editor: Bill Morelan
Copy Editors: Mary Alice Hill, Edward Sutherland • Story Editor: Tricia Schnell
Support Staff: Jeanne Jensen, Stephanie Schiltz

For more information about *A Reason For Spelling*®,
A Reason For Writing®, or other Concerned Communications curricula,
write to the address above or call:
(479) 549-9000

Dear Parent,

We are about to begin our first spelling unit containing five weekly lessons. A set of fifteen words will be studied each week. All the words will be reviewed in the sixth week. Values based on the Scriptures listed below will be taught in each lesson.

Lesson 1	Lesson 2	Lesson 3	Lesson 4	Lesson 5
answer	buzz	bother	clay	bread
began	cactus	chair	close	broke
berry	collar	change	cloth	crayon
body	crop	cheek	flag	cross
chest	deaf	cheese	flame	grab
chill	felt	cherry	flash	gray
gift	hello	north	glass	prayer
held	lamb	shock	glove	price
lift	pants	thankful	place	prize
list	stiff	thirteen	plain	proud
Monday	Sunday	Thursday	plant	skate
pick	twelve	whale	please	skin
puppy	wagon	wheat	plus	skip
test	west	whether	sleeve	spell
visit	window	whip	slice	spend
Ephesians 5:16	Ephesians 5:20	James 5:16	Philippians 3:1	Ephesians 1:4

A Preview

Write each word as your teacher says it.

1. _____

2. _____

3. _____

4. _____

5. _____

6. _____

7. _____

8. _____

9. _____

10. _____

11. _____

12. _____

13. _____

14. _____

15. _____

Scripture

Ephesians 5:16

Write each word in the correct word shape boxes. Next, in the word shape boxes, color the letter or letters that spell the short vowel sound in each word. Circle the words that have two syllables.

1. answer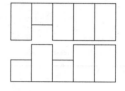

2. began

3. berry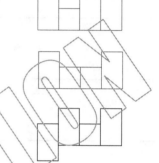

4. body

5. chest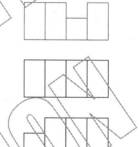

6. chill

7. gift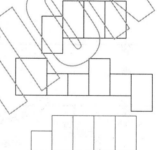

8. held

9. lift

10. list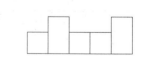

11. Monday

12. pick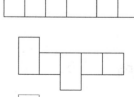

13. puppy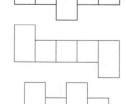

14. test

15. visit

C Hide and Seek

Place an **X** on a coin for each word you spell correctly.

Name _____

D Other Word Forms

Using the words below, follow the instructions given by your teacher.

answerable	bodies	hold	listlessness	tested
answering	bodily	holding	enlisted	testing
begin	chillier	holds	picked	tests
beginner	chilliest	lifted	pickier	visitation
beginning	chilliness	lifting	pickiest	visited
begun	chilly	listing	picking	visiting
berries	gifted	listless	puppies	visitor

E Fun Ways to Spell

Initial the box of each activity you finish.

1. [ ]

Spell your words with puzzles.

3. [ ]

Spell your words in rhythm.

2. [ ]

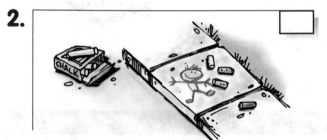

Spell your words with sidewalk chalk.

4. [ ]

Spell your words with play dough.

7

Name _____

Sentence Fun

Write the correct spelling word on the line to complete each sentence.

1. On _____, Mom parked at the school.

2. She did not _____ up the sign-man.

3. The sign he _____ said, "Will Work for Food."

4. Mom tried to _____ the boy's questions.

5. Soon, my dad _____ to pray for the sign-man.

6. Jesus went to _____ Zacchaeus.

ABC Order

Dictionary words are listed in alphabetical order. Words beginning with **a** come first, then words beginning with **b**, and so on. It is simple to find a word in the dictionary if you know about alphabetical order. Write the words from each group in alphabetical order.

test   puppy   list

1. _____   **2.** _____   **3.** _____

When words begin with the same letter, look at the second letter to put the words in alphabetical order. Write the words in alphabetical order.

gift   berry   body

4. _____   **5.** _____   **6.** _____

If the first two letters are the same, look at the third letter.
Write the words in alphabetical order.

chill   chest   lift

7. _____   **8.** _____   **9.** _____

Word Bank

answer	held	list	body	chill
begán	test	pick	Monday	chest
berry	gift	visit	puppy	lift

G Dictation

Name _____

Listen and write the missing words and punctuation.

1. _____ _____ _____ _____ _____ _____

_____ _____ _____ _____ _____ _

2. Please _____ _____ _____ _____

_____ _____ _

3. _____ sign _____ _____ _____ ," _____

" _____ _____ _____

H Proofreading

If a word is misspelled, fill in the oval by that word. If all the words are spelled correctly, fill in the oval by **no mistake**.

1. ○ red
○ anser
○ list
○ no mistake

2. ○ bus
○ held
○ pupy
○ no mistake

3. ○ lad
○ chil
○ tan
○ no mistake

4. ○ bary
○ ten
○ lift
○ no mistake

5. ○ pik
○ gift
○ God
○ no mistake

6. ○ chest
○ run
○ vizit
○ no mistake

7. ○ monday
○ began
○ list
○ no mistake

8. ○ held
○ man
○ fun
○ no mistake

9. ○ bodie
○ test
○ pot
○ no mistake

I

Name _____

Matthew and Alex want to ask God what the sign-man needs. Lead the way by moving one space for each word you or your team spells correctly from this week's word list.

Remember: Don't pass up a chance to do what Jesus would do.

J **Journaling**

Our text this week says to make the most of every opportunity for doing good. In your journal, make a list of people you can help.

Write each word as your teacher says it.

Name _____

1. _____

2. _____

3. _____

4. _____

5. _____

6. _____

7. _____

8. _____

9. _____

10. _____

11. _____

12. _____

13. _____

14. _____

15. _____

Scripture

Ephesians 5:20

Write each word in the correct word shape boxes. Next, in the word shape boxes, color the letter or letters that spell the short vowel sound in each word. Circle the words that have two syllables.

1. buzz

2. cactus

3. collar

4. crop

5. deaf

6. felt

7. hello

8. lamb

9. pants

10. stiff

11. Sunday

12. twelve

13. wagon

14. west

15. window

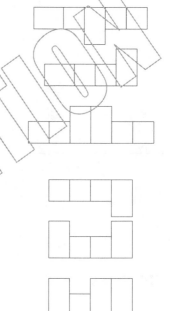

C Hide and Seek

Name _____

Place an **X** on a coin for each word you spell correctly.

D Other Word Forms

Using the words below, follow the instructions given by your teacher.

buzzed	cropping	feelingly	twelfth
buzzes	crops	hellos	wagons
buzzing	deafen	lambs	westerly
cacti	deafening	panting	western
collared	deafness	stiffens	westward
cropped	feel	stiffly	windowless
cropper	feeling	stiffness	windows

E Fun Ways to Spell

Initial the box of each activity you finish.

1. ☐

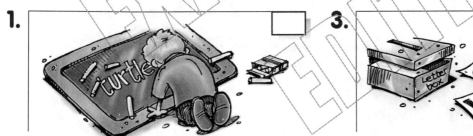

Spell your words with chalk.

3. ☐

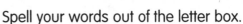

Spell your words out of the letter box.

2. ☐

Spell your words with glitter glue.

4. ☐

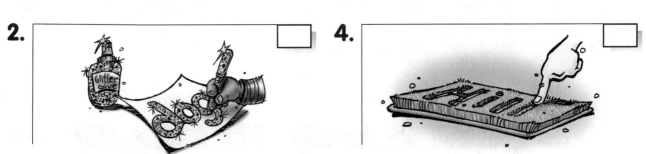

Spell your words on carpet.

Complete the Story

Matthew enjoyed the stories in his reading book about the settlers. Use each spelling word once to complete this story.

A covered **1.** _____ bounced along the trail. It was 1860 and the

Smiths were headed **2.** _____ to California. They hoped to find some

land to raise sheep, **3.** _____s, and **4.** _____s. The family had

been traveling since **5.** _____ night. Their legs felt **6.** _____ and

hard to move. Their dresses and **7.** _____ were covered with dust.

"Pa," Ma called. "Tell Billy to come here."

Pa suddenly realized Billy was missing! Right beside the **8.** _____

was their **9.** _____–year-old son. They **10.** _____ scared. Pa

and Ma had heard the **11.** _____ of rattlesnakes, but Billy wouldn't hear

them. He was **12.** _____.

"When did you last see Billy?" Pa asked.

"The last time we stopped, he ran off to look for rocks. I thought he got back in

the wagon with you."

"I should have paid more attention," Pa sighed and ran his finger around his

13. _____. He jumped from the wagon and grabbed his rifle.

"Wait for me," Ma cried. "I'm coming with you."

They shaded their eyes and looked around. Suddenly, they heard a voice call,

" **14.** _____." Ma and Pa whirled around, and there was Billy, perched

on the back of the wagon. With relief they hugged him as Ma exclaimed, "Next

time, I'll look out the back **15.** _____ before I panic!"

Words with Short Vowels

Lesson

2

Word Bank

buzz	crop	hello	stiff	wagon
cactus	deaf	lamb	Sunday	west
collar	felt	pants	twelve	window

G Dictation

Listen and write the missing words and punctuation.

1. _____ sign–_____ wore baggy _____ _

2. ___ _____ _____ _____ _____ standing

___ _____ _ _

3. Jesus _____ _____ _____ heal ___

_____ _____ _

H Proofreading

If a word is misspelled, fill in the oval by that word. If all the words are spelled correctly, fill in the oval by **no mistake**.

1. ⃝ twelve
   ⃝ gift
   ⃝ buz
   ⃝ no mistake

2. ⃝ west
   ⃝ caktus
   ⃝ puppy
   ⃝ no mistake

3. ⃝ collar
   ⃝ felt
   ⃝ berry
   ⃝ no mistake

4. ⃝ krop
   ⃝ wagon
   ⃝ chill
   ⃝ no mistake

5. ⃝ body
   ⃝ def
   ⃝ window
   ⃝ no mistake

6. ⃝ window
   ⃝ hello
   ⃝ test
   ⃝ no mistake

7. ⃝ visit
   ⃝ pants
   ⃝ lamm
   ⃝ no mistake

8. ⃝ stiff
   ⃝ answer
   ⃝ Monday
   ⃝ no mistake

9. ⃝ Sundy
   ⃝ chest
   ⃝ pick
   ⃝ no mistake

I | Game

Name _____

Fill in the secret phrase by correctly spelling the words from this week's word list.

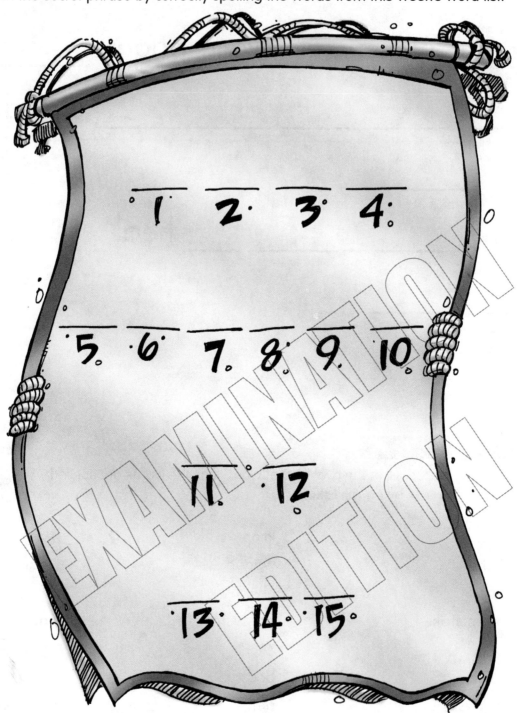

___ ___ ___ ___
1   2   3   4

___ ___ ___ ___ ___ ___
5   6   7   8   9   10

___ ___
11   12

___ ___ ___
13   14   15

Remember: Keep a thankful heart.

J | Journaling

In your journal, make a list of things that describe you. When your list is done, compare it with a classmate's. Circle everything that is different about your lists. Take time to thank God for the differences that make you special!

A Preview

Write each word as your teacher says it.

1. _____

2. _____

3. _____

4. _____

5. _____

6. _____

7. _____

8. _____

9. _____

10. _____

11. _____

12. _____

13. _____

14. _____

15. _____

Scripture

James 5:16

Name _____

Write each word in the correct word shape boxes. Next, in the word shape boxes, color the letters that spell the consonant digraph or digraphs in each word. Circle the words that end with a digraph.

1. bother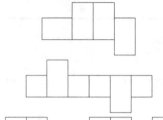

2. chair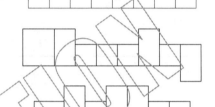

3. change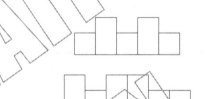

4. cheek

5. cheese

6. cherry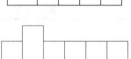

7. north

8. shock

9. thankful

10. thirteen

11. Thursday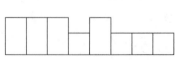

12. whale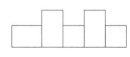

13. wheat

14. whether

15. whip

C Hide and Seek

Name _____

Place an **X** on a coin for each word you spell correctly.

D Other Word Forms

Using the words below, follow the instructions given by your teacher.

bothering	changing	cheesy	shocking	whaled
bothersome	exchange	cherries	shockingly	whaler
chaired	cheekier	northerly	thankfully	whales
chairman	cheekiest	northern	thankfulness	whaling
changeable	cheekily	northward	thankless	whipped
changed	cheeky	shocked	thirteenth	whipping

E Fun Ways to Spell

Initial the box of each activity you finish.

1.

Spell your words with pictures.

2.

Spell your words with lemon juice.

3.

Spell your words out loud.

4.

Spell your words with pipe cleaners.

Name _____

Word Sort

Write each spelling word under the correct digraph heading. If a word fits under two headings, write it under both..

	th		ch		wh		sh

th **ch** **wh** **sh**

1. _____   7. _____   12. _____   16. _____

2. _____   8. _____   13. _____

3. _____   9. _____   14. _____

4. _____   10. _____   15. _____

5. _____   11. _____

6. _____

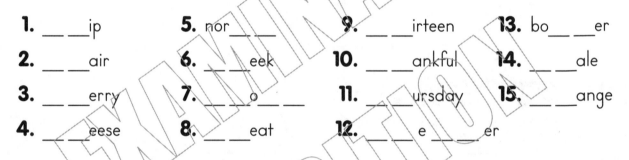

Missing Letters

Write the consonant digraph for each spelling word.

1. ___ ___ ip   5. nor ___ ___   9. ___ ___ irteen   13. bo ___ ___ er

2. ___ ___ air   6. ___ ___ eek   10. ___ ___ ankful   14. ___ ___ ale

3. ___ ___ erry   7. ___ ___ o ___ ___   11. ___ ___ ursday   15. ___ ___ ange

4. ___ ___ eese   8. ___ ___ eat   12. ___ e ___ ___ er

Dictionary Skills

There are two words at the top of each page in a dictionary. They are called guide words. The guide word on the left is the first word on that page. The guide word on the right is the last word on that page. Guide words help you find words in a dictionary. Pretend the bolded words below are guide words on a dictionary page. Write the spelling words that would be found on a page with these guide words.

chain cheer   **whack which**   **than thy**

1. _____   4. _____   7. _____

2. _____   5. _____   8. _____

3. _____   6. _____   9. _____

Word Bank

bother	cheek	north	thirteen	wheat
chair	cheese	shock	Thursday	whether
change	cherry	thankful	whale	whip

G Dictation

Name _____

Listen and write the missing words and punctuation.

1. Mr. Wilson ____ ____ ____ ____

   ____ tire _

2. Harrison ate ____ ____ ____

   hot ____ _

3. Mr. Potter ____ ____

   ____ ____ ____ _

H Proofreading

If a word is misspelled, fill in the oval by that word. If all the words are spelled correctly, fill in the oval by **no mistake**.

1. ⬭ bother
   ⬭ wip
   ⬭ crop
   ⬭ no mistake

2. ⬭ wether
   ⬭ deaf
   ⬭ lamb
   ⬭ no mistake

3. ⬭ weet
   ⬭ cheek
   ⬭ buzz
   ⬭ no mistake

4. ⬭ Thursday
   ⬭ cactus
   ⬭ thirteen
   ⬭ no mistake

5. ⬭ north
   ⬭ berry
   ⬭ thankfull
   ⬭ no mistake

6. ⬭ chery
   ⬭ whale
   ⬭ pick
   ⬭ no mistake

7. ⬭ felt
   ⬭ cheeze
   ⬭ stiff
   ⬭ no mistake

8. ⬭ change
   ⬭ wagon
   ⬭ lift
   ⬭ no mistake

9. ⬭ window
   ⬭ shock
   ⬭ chare
   ⬭ no mistake

I | Game

John Potter and his family will follow Brad Wilson to the Knowlton Elementary work bee. Lead the way by moving one space for each word you or your team spells correctly from this week's word list.

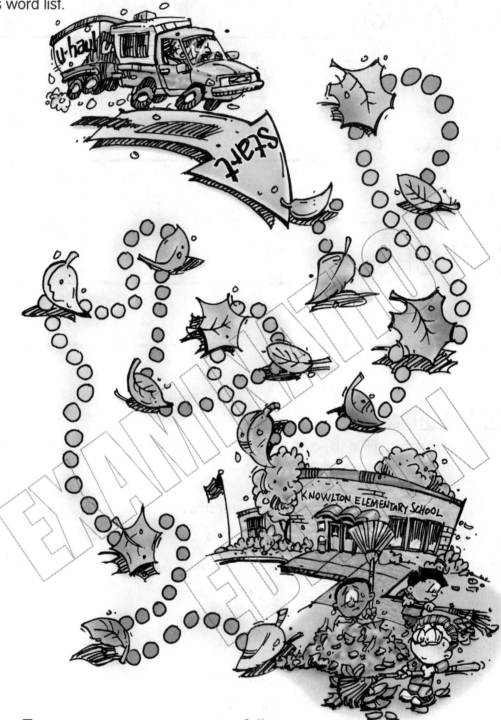

Remember: Earnest prayer is very powerful!

J | Journaling

In your journal, make a list of things you would like to earnestly pray about.

A Preview

Write each word as your teacher says it.

Name _____

1. _____

2. _____

3. _____

4. _____

5. _____

6. _____

7. _____

8. _____

9. _____

10. _____

11. _____

12. _____

13. _____

14. _____

15. _____

Scripture

Philippians 3:1

B **Word Shapes**

Name _____

Write each word in the correct word shape boxes. Next, in the word shape boxes, color the letters that spell the consonant cluster in each word. Circle the words that begin with a consonant cluster and end with a digraph.

1. clay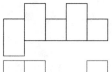

2. close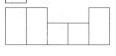

3. cloth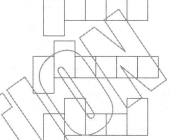

4. flag

5. flame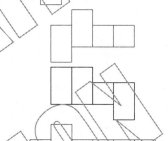

6. flash

7. glass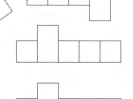

8. glove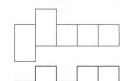

9. place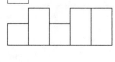

10. plain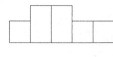

11. plant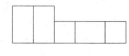

12. please

13. plus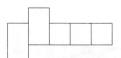

14. sleeve

15. slice

C Hide and Seek

Place an **X** on a coin for each word you spell correctly.

D Other Word Forms

Using the words below, follow the instructions given by your teacher.

closed	clothing	glassful	plainness	sleeves
closely	cloths	glassy	planted	sliced
closeness	flagged	gloved	planter	slices
closer	flagging	placed	planting	slicing
closest	flames	placement	pleased	
closing	flaming	places	pleasing	
clothe	flashing	placing	pleasingly	
clothed	flashy	plainly	sleeveless	

E Fun Ways to Spell

Initial the box of each activity you finish.

1.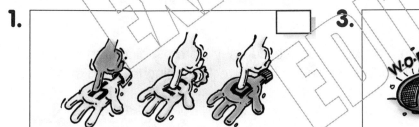

Spell your words in your classmate's hand.

3.

Spell your words using a tape recorder.

2.

Spell your words with paper cups.

4.

Spell your words with magazine clippings.

F Working with Words

Name _____

Rhyming Words

Write the spelling word that rhymes with the words below.

1. spice _____

2. play _____

3. grain _____

4. broth _____

5. slant _____

6. sneeze _____

7. space _____

8. grieve _____

9. shove _____

10. blame _____

11. class _____

12. clash _____

13. brag _____

14. rose _____

15. truss _____

Clues

Write the spelling word that matches each clue.

1. shut _____

2. mitten _____

3. fabric _____

4. gleam _____

5. simple _____

6. area _____

7. satisfy _____

8. fragile _____

9. fire _____

10. cut _____

11. banner _____

12. play dough _____

13. add _____

14. shrub _____

15. jacket _____

Dictionary Skills

The words listed and explained in a dictionary are called entry words. A dictionary tells what words mean and how they are used. Draw a line to the correct meaning for each dictionary entry below.

1. close   space for a person or thing

2. slice   to shut

3. place   to make glad

4. please   a thin flat piece cut from something

Word Bank

clay	flag	glass	plain	plus
close	flame	glove	plant	sleeve
cloth	flash	place	please	slice

G Dictation

Name _____

Listen and write the missing words and punctuation.

1. Kristin _____ ___ ____ __ ____

_____ sill _

2. _____ __ __ ____ __ ____

____ shot _

3. Miss ten Boom's guard _____

____ ___ _____ _

H Proofreading

If a word is misspelled, fill in the oval by that word. If all the words are spelled correctly, fill in the oval by **no mistake**.

1.
- cloth
- cherry
- klay
- no mistake

4.
- glass
- plant
- thankful
- no mistake

7.
- plain
- chair
- hello
- no mistake

2.
- wheat
- klose
- flash
- no mistake

5.
- gluv
- plus
- Sunday
- no mistake

8.
- change
- pleaze
- twelve
- no mistake

3.
- flaem
- flag
- whether
- no mistake

6.
- whip
- plase
- slice
- no mistake

9.
- sleave
- west
- pants
- no mistake

I Game

Christopher and Kristin need to get shots today. Lead the way to the doctor's office by moving one space for each word you or your team spells correctly from this week's word list.

Remember: God wants us to find happiness in Him no matter what!

J Journaling

In your journal, write about some times when it might be hard to be glad. Then write a prayer asking God's help to always be glad in Him.

A Preview

Write each word as your teacher says it.

Name _____

1. _____

2. _____

3. _____

4. _____

5. _____

6. _____

7. _____

8. _____

9. _____

10. _____

11. _____

12. _____

13. _____

14. _____

15. _____

Scripture

Ephesians 1:4

B Word Shapes

Name _____

Write each word in the correct word shape boxes. Next, in the word shape boxes, color the letters that spell the consonant cluster in each word. Circle the word that has two syllables.

1. bread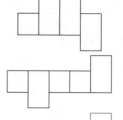

2. broke

3. crayon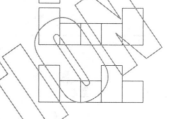

4. cross

5. grab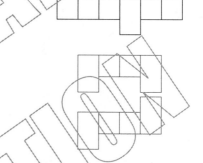

6. gray

7. prayer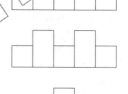

8. price

9. prize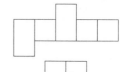

10. proud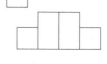

11. skate

12. skin

13. skip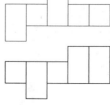

14. spell

15. spend

C Hide and Seek

Name _____

Place an **X** on a coin for each word you spell correctly.

D Other Word Forms

Using the words below, follow the instructions given by your teacher.

breaded	crossword	priceless	skinned	spelling
break	grabbed	pricing	skinning	spender
breakable	grabbing	prized	skinny	spending
breaking	grayish	prizing	skipped	spent
broken	grayness	proudly	skipping	
crossed	prayerful	skater	skips	
crossing	prayerfully	skates	spelled	
crosswise	priced	skating	speller	

E Fun Ways to Spell

Initial the box of each activity you finish.

1.

Spell your words with markers.

3.

Spell your words while snapping.

2.

Spell your words with letter tiles.

4.

Spell your words with paint.

F **Working with Words**

Name _____

Secret Words

Use the clues to write the words in the puzzle. Then write the boxed letters on the lines below to find the words from this week's Scripture.

1. The skies are cloudy and __.
2. Jesus died on a __.
3. __ is used to make sandwiches.
4. You can color with a __.

5. The glass fell and __.
6. I learn to __ words so I can write.
7. We talk to God in __.
8. Mom is __ of me.

9. I like to __ time with Dad.
10. I fell a lot when I learned to __.
11. It is not polite to __ food.
12. Mom got a lot of spinach for a good __.
13. I had to __ school when I was sick.
14. When I fell, I scraped the __ on my knee.

__ __ __ __ h __ __ __ __ __ __ o __ __ H __ __

Word Bank

bread	cross	prayer	proud	skip
broke	grab	price	skate	spell
crayon	gray	prize	skin	spend

G Dictation

Name _____

Listen and write the missing words and punctuation.

1. _____ _____ _____ _____ _____

 _____ _____ _____

2. _____ _____ _____ _____ _____

 _____ _____ _____ _____

3. _____ _____ _____ _____ _____ _____

 _____ _____ _____

H Proofreading

If a word is misspelled, fill in the oval by that word. If all the words are spelled correctly, fill in the oval by **no mistake**.

1. ○ bread
   ○ grab
   ○ sleeve
   ○ no mistake

2. ○ price
   ○ brocke
   ○ please
   ○ no mistake

3. ○ craeon
   ○ skate
   ○ cheese
   ○ no mistake

4. ○ skin
   ○ clay
   ○ kross
   ○ no mistake

5. ○ spell
   ○ grae
   ○ close
   ○ no mistake

6. ○ praer
   ○ spend
   ○ place
   ○ no mistake

7. ○ flame
   ○ glove
   ○ prise
   ○ no mistake

8. ○ list
   ○ body
   ○ prowd
   ○ no mistake

9. ○ skip
   ○ collar
   ○ bother
   ○ no mistake

I | Game

Name _____

Glue on a piece of the puzzle-picture for each word you or your team spells correctly from this week's word list.

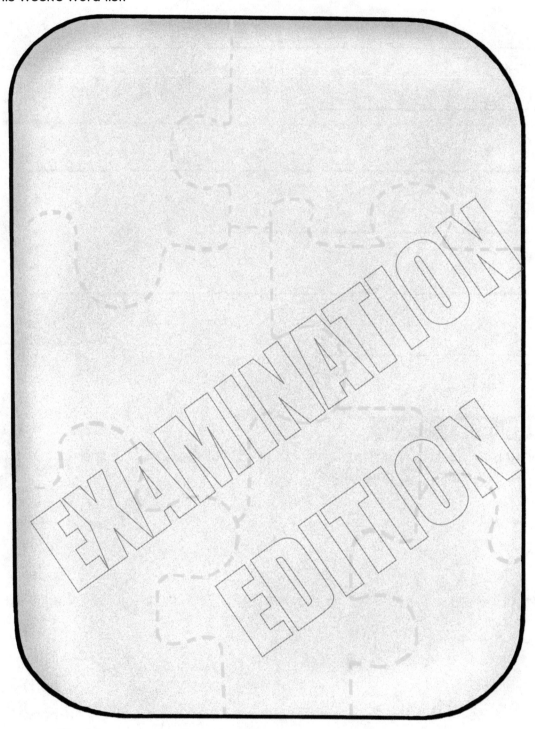

Remember: God has always loved you!

J | Journaling

In your journal, write about your family. Write about the family who lives in your home. Write about how often you see family members like your grandparents, aunts, uncles, and cousins.

A Test-Words

Name _____

Write each spelling word on the line as your teacher says it.

1. _____   7. _____

2. _____   8. _____

3. _____   9. _____

4. _____   10. _____

5. _____   11. _____

6. _____   12. _____

B Test-Sentences

Write the sentences on the lines below, correcting each misspelled word, as well as all capitalization and punctuation errors. There are two misspelled words in each sentence.

the def boy could not hear the buz of the timer

1. _____

Please plaice the gluv back in the drawer?

2. _____

the doughnuts had cream cheeze and cherrie fillings,

3. _____

C Test-Dictation

Name _____

Listen and write the missing words and punctuation.

1. ___ ___ ___ ___ pledge ___ ___ ___ ___

2. ___ candle ___ ___ ___ bright_

3. ___ ___ ___ ___ snake ___

   ___ ___ ___ ___

4. ___ ___ ___ ___ ___

   ___ sticker_

D Test-Proofreading

If a word is misspelled, fill in the oval by that word. If all the words are spelled correctly, fill in the oval by **no mistake**.

1. ◯ Monday
   ◯ deaf
   ◯ body
   ◯ no mistake

2. ◯ hello
   ◯ north
   ◯ cactis
   ◯ no mistake

3. ◯ wip
   ◯ thankful
   ◯ please
   ◯ no mistake

4. ◯ slice
   ◯ whale
   ◯ spend
   ◯ no mistake

5. ◯ glove
   ◯ spel
   ◯ berry
   ◯ no mistake

6. ◯ krop
   ◯ shock
   ◯ cheese
   ◯ no mistake

7. ◯ lamb
   ◯ prayer
   ◯ wheat
   ◯ no mistake

8. ◯ west
   ◯ chair
   ◯ chanje
   ◯ no mistake

9. ◯ north
   ◯ plus
   ◯ cross
   ◯ no mistake

E Test-Shapes

If a word is misspelled, color the acorn by that word.

shok

test

plus

cheek

graye

plant

priez

list

scip

lift

west

thertean

panst

skin

F Writing Assessment

Write a letter to God. Write about the things He has done for you. Thank Him for what He has done. Tell Him how you feel about His great love.

_____

_____

_____

_____

_____

_____

_____

_____

Scripture

Ephesians 1:11

G Test-Sentences

Name _____

Write the sentences on the lines below, correcting each misspelled word, as well as all capitalization and punctuation errors. There are two misspelled words in each sentence.

i'd like a weet roll, pleeze

1. _____

On thersday we can vizit the farm.

2. _____

Mom and dad gave us a pupie for a gitf

3. _____

H Test-Words

Write each spelling word on the line as your teacher says it.

1. _____   7. _____

2. _____   8. _____

3. _____   9. _____

4. _____   10. _____

5. _____   11. _____

6. _____   12. _____

If a word is spelled correctly, fill in the oval under **Correct**. If the word is misspelled, fill in the oval under **Incorrect**, and spell the word correctly on the blank.

Correct   Incorrect

1. berry   ⬭   ⬭   _____

2. chill   ⬭   ⬭   _____

3. kross   ⬭   ⬭   _____

4. helo   ⬭   ⬭   _____

5. plian   ⬭   ⬭   _____

6. skate   ⬭   ⬭   _____

7. stif   ⬭   ⬭   _____

8. wether   ⬭   ⬭   _____

9. bother   ⬭   ⬭   _____

10. prayer   ⬭   ⬭   _____

11. wagun   ⬭   ⬭   _____

12. whale   ⬭   ⬭   _____

Review

Lesson

6

Score points for each review word or Other Word Form you or your team spells correctly.

Remember: God is pleased with us for Jesus' sake.

Spelling Is Fun!

This certificate is awarded to

_____

for practicing the following words, by doing terrific
spelling activities, and playing great spelling games!

Date _____

answer	buzz	bother	clay	bread
began	cactus	chair	close	broke
berry	collar	change	cloth	crayon
body	crop	cheek	flag	cross
chest	deaf	cheese	flame	grab
chill	felt	cherry	flash	gray
gift	hello	north	glass	prayer
held	lamb	shock	glove	price
lift	pants	thankful	place	prize
list	stiff	thirteen	plain	proud
Monday	Sunday	Thursday	plant	skate
pick	twelve	whale	please	skin
puppy	wagon	wheat	plus	skip
test	west	whether	sleeve	spell
visit	window	whip	slice	spend

A Reason For Spelling®

Dear Parent,

We are about to begin a new spelling unit containing five weekly lessons. A set of fifteen words will be studied each week. All the words will be reviewed in the sixth week. Values based on the Scriptures listed below will be taught in each lesson.

Lesson 7	Lesson 8	Lesson 9	Lesson 10	Lesson 11
scrap	address	aunt	crash	bright
scratch	butter	behind	earth	caught
scream	classroom	belong	fresh	chalk
screen	happen	bump	hatch	clothes
scrub	ladder	drank	kick	half
spread	lesson	front	match	knee
spring	merry	grandfather	neck	knot
straight	million	grandmother	porch	neighbor
strange	really	husband	ranch	sidewalk
straw	rubber	ink	rush	sight
stream	smell	sang	sack	though
street	sudden	stamp	sandwich	thumb
string	sunny	wind	splash	Wednesday
strong	supper	wing	switch	whole
threw	unhappy	young	teacher	wrap

| 1 Peter 3:10 | Ephesians 5:2 | Philippians 4:4,5 | 1 Peter 4:8 | 1 Peter 4:10 |

A Preview

Write each word as your teacher says it.

Name _____

1. _____

2. _____

3. _____

4. _____

5. _____

6. _____

7. _____

8. _____   12. _____

9. _____   13. _____

10. _____   14. _____

11. _____   15. _____

Scripture

I Peter 3:10

B Word Shapes

Name _____

Write each word in the correct word shape boxes. Next, in the word shape boxes, color the letters that spell the beginning consonant cluster in each word. Circle the word that does not begin with /s/.

1. scrap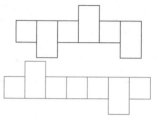

2. scratch

3. scream

4. screen

5. scrub

6. spread

7. spring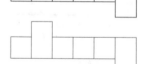

8. straight

9. strange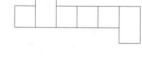

10. straw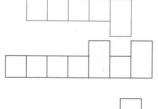

11. stream

12. street

13. string

14. strong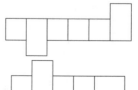

15. threw

C Hide and Seek

Name _____

Place an **X** on a coin for each word you spell correctly.

D Other Word Forms

Using the words below, follow the instructions given by your teacher.

scrapped	screening	springs	strangest	strung
scrapping	scrubbed	springy	streamer	stronger
scraps	scrubber	sprung	streamlined	strongest
scratched	scrubbing	straighten	streams	strongly
scratches	scrubby	straightening	streets	throw
scratchy	spreader	straightway	stringed	throwing
screamed	spreading	strangely	stringier	thrown
screaming	sprang	strangeness	stringing	
screams	springing	stranger	stringy	

E Fun Ways to Spell

Initial the box of each activity you finish.

1.

Spell your words with puzzles.

3.

Spell your words in rhythm.

2.

Spell your words with sidewalk chalk.

4.

Spell your words with play dough.

45

F Working with Words

Name _____

Spelling Clues

Write the correct spelling word on the line.

1. The little word **on** is in what bigger word?

2. The little word **rat** is in what bigger word?

3. The little word **range** is in what bigger word?

4. The little word **rap** is in what bigger word?

5. The little word **tree** is in what bigger word?

6. The little word **rub** is in what bigger word?

7. The little word **raw** is in what bigger word?

8. The little word **read** is in what bigger word?

9. The little word **ring** is in what bigger words?

10. Write the words in which /ē/ is spelled **ee**.

11. Write the words in which /ē/ is spelled **ea**.

12. Write the word in which /e/ is spelled **ea**.

1. _____

2. _____

3. _____

4. _____

5. _____

6. _____

7. _____

8. _____

9. _____

_____

10. _____

_____

11. _____

_____

12. _____

Missing Letters

Write the consonant cluster for each spelling word.

1. __ __ __ een

2. __ __ __ eet

3. __ __ ead

4. __ __ __ eam

5. __ __ __ eam

6. __ __ __ aw

7. __ __ __ ew

8. __ __ __ ing

9. __ __ __ ing

10. __ __ __ aight

11. __ __ __ ange

12. __ __ __ ong

Word Bank

scrap	screen	spring	straw	string
scratch	scrub	straight	stream	strong
scream	spread	strange	street	threw

G **Dictation**   Name _____

Listen and write the missing words and punctuation.

1. Tommy's _____ _____ _____

_____ sundae __

2. Tommy ___ _____ ____ ___

___ __ lie __

3. ___ _____ _____ _____ ___

____ base __

H **Proofreading**

If a word is misspelled, fill in the oval by that word. If all the words are spelled correctly, fill in the oval by **no mistake**.

1. ◯ scrach
   ◯ straw
   ◯ broke
   ◯ no mistake

2. ◯ gray
   ◯ proud
   ◯ screem
   ◯ no mistake

3. ◯ prayer
   ◯ cross
   ◯ skate
   ◯ no mistake

4. ◯ spread
   ◯ street
   ◯ prize
   ◯ no mistake

5. ◯ strate
   ◯ spring
   ◯ flag
   ◯ no mistake

6. ◯ string
   ◯ streem
   ◯ scrap
   ◯ no mistake

7. ◯ stranj
   ◯ scrub
   ◯ glass
   ◯ no mistake

8. ◯ north
   ◯ thrue
   ◯ held
   ◯ no mistake

9. ◯ stong
   ◯ plain
   ◯ plus
   ◯ no mistake

I Game

Tommy needs to tell Mr. Valentino the truth. Lead the way by moving one space for each word you or your team spells correctly from this week's word list.

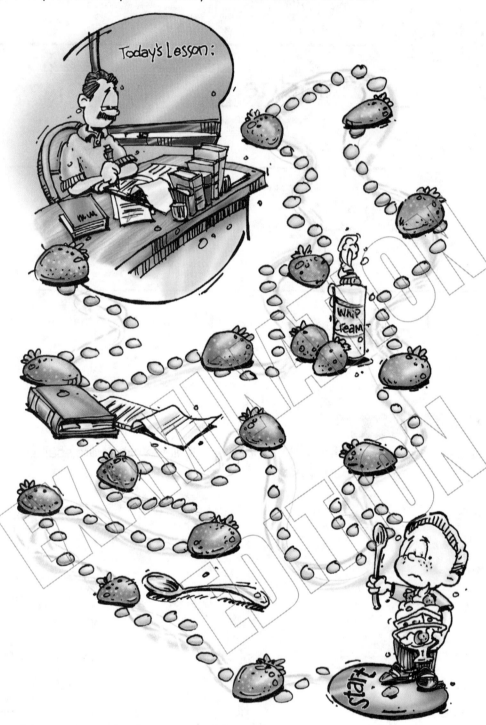

Remember: You cannot be happy and be a liar.

J Journaling

In your journal, write about a time when you were tempted to lie. If you didn't lie, tell how you chose to be truthful. If you did tell a lie, tell how you felt about lying. (If you haven't made your lie right, ask God to help you do that, so you can be truly happy.)

A Preview

Write each word as your teacher says it.

Name _____

1. _____

2. _____

3. _____

4. _____

5. _____

6. _____

7. _____

8. _____

9. _____

10. _____

11. _____

12. _____

13. _____

14. _____

15. _____

Scripture

Ephesians 5:2

B Word Shapes

Write each word in the correct word shape boxes. Next, in the word shape boxes, color the double consonant in each word.

1. address

2. butter

3. classroom

4. happen

5. ladder

6. lesson

7. merry

8. million

9. really

10. rubber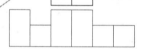

11. smell

12. sudden

13. sunny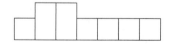

14. supper

15. unhappy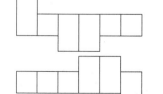

C Hide and Seek

Name _____

Place an **X** on a coin for each word you spell correctly.

D Other Word Forms

Using the words below, follow the instructions given by your teacher.

addresses	happy	millionth	sunnier
addressing	ladders	rubberize	sunniest
buttery	lessons	rubbery	unhappily
classrooms	merrier	smelled	unhappiness
happened	merriest	smelling	
happening	merrily	smelly	
happier	millionaire	suddenly	
happiness	millions	suddenness	

E Fun Ways to Spell

Initial the box of each activity you finish.

1.

Spell your words with chalk.

3.

Spell your words out of the letter box.

2.

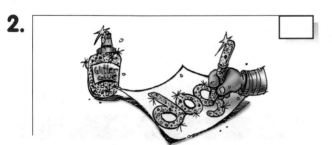

Spell your words with glitter glue.

4.

Spell your words on carpet.

F **Working with Words**

Name _____

Syllables

An entry word in the dictionary is often divided into syllables.

syl•la•ble [**sil**′ə′bəl] n.   A unit of sound in a word. A syllable contains a vowel and possibly one or more consonants.

These are examples of entry words. Count how many syllables each word has and write the number on the line.

1. col•lar _____   **2.** cloth _____   **3.** Sat•ur•day _____

Find each of the words below in the dictionary. Write them in syllables, putting a dot between the syllables.

1. address _____   **7.** butter _____

2. happen _____   **8.** ladder _____

3. lesson _____   **9.** merry _____

4. million _____   **10.** rubber _____

5. sudden _____   **11.** sunny _____

6. supper _____   **12.** really _____

What pattern did you notice when these words were divided into syllables?

13. _____

Write the word that has three syllables, putting a dot between the syllables.

14. unhappy _____

Write the spelling word that has only one syllable.

15. _____

Word Bank

address	happen	merry	rubber	sunny
butter	ladder	million	smell	supper
classroom	lesson	really	sudden	unhappy

G Dictation

Name _____

Listen **and** write the missing words and punctuation.

1. _____ _____ _____ _____ __

_____ _____ ___ _____ __

2. Daniel _____ _____ _____ _____

_____ __ _____ ___

3. _____ nurse _____ _____ _____ _____

__ _____ _____ __

H Proofreading

If a word is misspelled, fill in the oval by that word. If all the words are spelled correctly, fill in the oval by **no mistake**.

1. ⬭ address
   ⬭ butter
   ⬭ scratch
   ⬭ no mistake

2. ⬭ clasroom
   ⬭ sunny
   ⬭ spell
   ⬭ no mistake

3. ⬭ happin
   ⬭ screen
   ⬭ threw
   ⬭ no mistake

4. ⬭ smell
   ⬭ skin
   ⬭ laddir
   ⬭ no mistake

5. ⬭ skip
   ⬭ lessun
   ⬭ straight
   ⬭ no mistake

6. ⬭ supper
   ⬭ rubber
   ⬭ merrie
   ⬭ no mistake

7. ⬭ milion
   ⬭ stream
   ⬭ strong
   ⬭ no mistake

8. ⬭ unhappy
   ⬭ grab
   ⬭ realy
   ⬭ no mistake

9. ⬭ suddin
   ⬭ Thursday
   ⬭ slice
   ⬭ no mistake

I Game

James and Tommy want to follow Jesus' example and treat Daniel with love. Lead the way by moving one space for each word you or your team spells correctly from this week's word list.

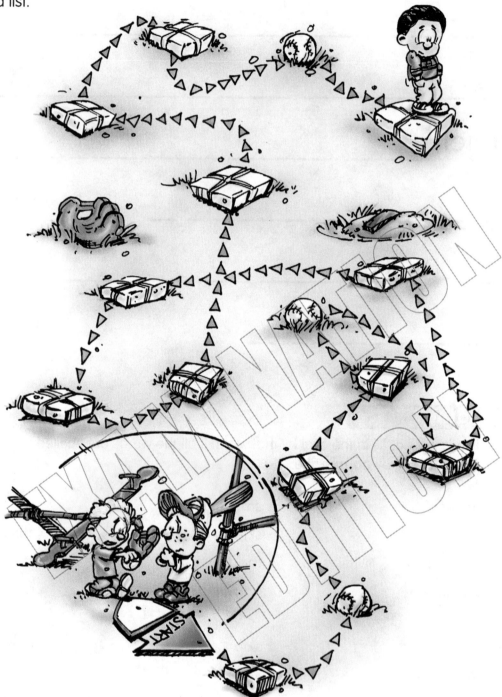

Remember: When you love others, you are following in Jesus' steps.

J Journaling

In your journal, write at least six ways you can follow Christ's example of kindness, here in our classroom.

A Preview

Write each word as your teacher says it.

1. _____

2. _____

3. _____

4. _____

5. _____

6. _____

7. _____

8. _____

9. _____

10. _____

11. _____

12. _____

13. _____

14. _____

15. _____

Scripture

Philippians 4:4,5

B **Word Shapes**

Name _____

Write each word in the correct word shape boxes. Next, in the word shape boxes, color the consonant cluster with **m** or **n** in each word. Circle the words that have more than one consonant cluster.

1. aunt

2. behind

3. belong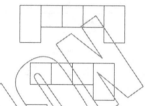

4. bump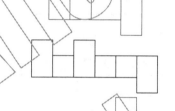

5. drank

6. front

7. grandfather

8. grandmother

9. husband

10. ink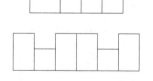

11. sang

12. stamp

13. wind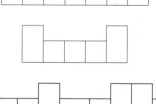

14. wing

15. young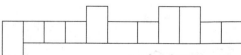

C Hide and Seek

Name _____

Place an **X** on a coin for each word you spell correctly.

D Other Word Forms

Using the words below, follow the instructions given by your teacher.

aunts	drink	stamped	winging
belongings	drunk	stamping	wings
belongs	inking	stamps	younger
bumped	inky	winded	youngest
bumpily	sing	winding	youngster
bumping	singing	windy	
bumpy	songs	winged	

E Fun Ways to Spell

Initial the box of each activity you finish.

1.

Spell your words with pictures.

3.

Spell your words out loud.

2.

Spell your words with lemon juice.

4.

Spell your words with pipe cleaners.

F Working with Words

Name _____

Spelling Clues

Write the spelling words that contain the cluster **mp**.

1. _____   2. _____

Write the spelling words that contain the cluster **nd**.

3. _____   4. _____

5. _____   6. _____

7. _____

Write the spelling words that contain the cluster **ng**.

8. _____   9. _____

10. _____   11. _____

Proofing

Use proofreading marks to show the errors in the paragraph below. Write the seven misspelled words correctly on the lines.

⬭ word is misspelled	∧ word or words missing

When my ant Ida was a girl, she lived her granfather and grandmoter.

She often found yung animals that had been hurt, and brought them home care

for. One day she found a bird with a broken wimg. She knew it did not truly

beloung to her, but she cared for it gently until had healed. She then took it

back to the woods beehind the barn and set it free.

1. _____   4. _____   6. _____

2. _____   5. _____   7. _____

3. _____

Word Bank

aunt	bump	grandfather	ink	wind
behind	drank	grandmother	sang	wing
belong	front	husband	stamp	young

G Dictation

Name _____

Listen and write the missing words and punctuation.

1. Beth _____ ____ _____ _____ _____ _____

"

_____ _____ __

2. Beth _____ _____ _____ _____

_____ _____ _____ __

3. _____ _____ _____ _____ _____ _____

_____ _____ _____

H Proofreading

If a word is misspelled, fill in the oval by that word. If all the words are spelled correctly, fill in the oval by **no mistake**.

1. ◯ belong
   ◯ aunt
   ◯ ladder
   ◯ no mistake

2. ◯ bihind
   ◯ wing
   ◯ really
   ◯ no mistake

3. ◯ merry
   ◯ drakn
   ◯ strange
   ◯ no mistake

4. ◯ bump
   ◯ classroom
   ◯ granfather
   ◯ no mistake

5. ◯ granmother
   ◯ ink
   ◯ lesson
   ◯ no mistake

6. ◯ sang
   ◯ huzband
   ◯ million
   ◯ no mistake

7. ◯ sudden
   ◯ supper
   ◯ frunt
   ◯ no mistake

8. ◯ stanp
   ◯ wind
   ◯ street
   ◯ no mistake

9. ◯ happen
   ◯ yung
   ◯ rubber
   ◯ no mistake

I Game

Go along with the Hill family as they shop for a new vehicle. Move one space for each word you or your team spells correctly from this week's word list.

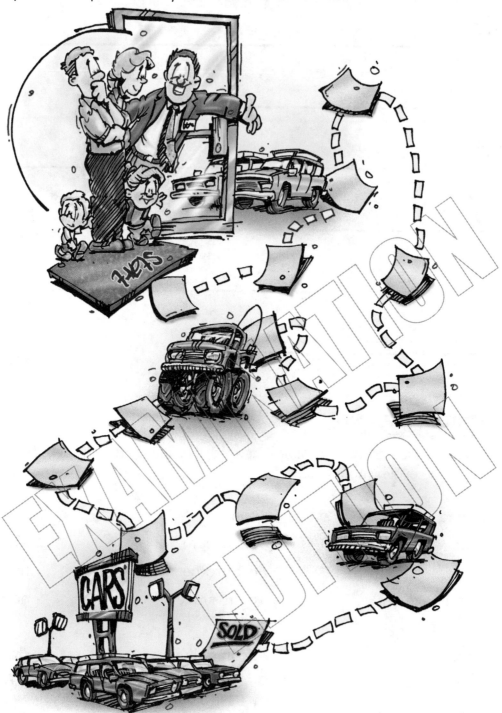

Remember: Be happy and full of joy!

J Journaling

Write a paragraph about all the things you can rejoice about.

A Preview

Write each word as your teacher says it.

1. _____

2. _____

3. _____

4. _____

5. _____

6. _____

7. _____

8. _____

9. _____

10. _____

11. _____

12. _____

13. _____

14. _____

15. _____

Scripture

I Peter 4:8

B **Word Shapes**

Name _____

Write each word in the correct word shape boxes. Next, in the word shape boxes, color the consonant digraph in each word. Circle the words that have a consonant cluster and digraph.

1. crash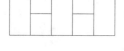

2. earth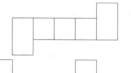

3. fresh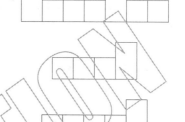

4. hatch

5. kick

6. match

7. neck

8. porch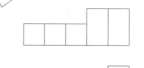

9. ranch

10. rush

11. sack

12. sandwich

13. splash

14. switch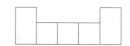

15. teacher

C Hide and Seek

Place an **X** on a coin for each word you spell correctly.

Name _____

D Other Word Forms

Using the words below, follow the instructions given by your teacher.

crashed	refresh	matches	sacked	switched
crashes	hatched	matching	sacker	switching
crashing	hatches	rematch	sacking	teach
earthen	hatching	necks	sandwiched	teaches
earthly	kicked	porches	sandwiches	teaching
freshen	kicking	ranches	splashed	
freshly	kicks	rushes	splashes	
freshness	matched	rushing	splashing	

E Fun Ways to Spell

Initial the box of each activity you finish.

1.

Spell your words in your classmate's hand.

3.

Spell your words using a tape recorder.

2.

Spell your words with paper cups.

4.

Spell your words with magazine clippings.

F **Working with Words**

Name _____

Word Sort

Write each spelling word under the correct consonant digraph heading.

	ch		sh		tch
1. _____		5. _____		9. _____
2. _____		6. _____		10. _____
3. _____		7. _____		11. _____
4. _____		8. _____		

Proofing

Use proofreading marks to show the errors in the paragraph below. Write the nine misspelled words correctly on the lines.

◯ word is misspelled	⋀ word or words missing	≡ capitalize letter

One day we decided play kickball at recess. Hal ate his sandwitch quickly and tossed his empty lunch sak in trash can. he ran outside with the ball and began to kitck it around, waiting for the rest of to finish lunch. The ground was damp the recent rain, and hal landed with a slpash when his foot a small puddle. The ball flew through the air and hit a dead limb on the old oak tree that stood the school. our teecher ran off the portch in a rusch when he saw limb fall to the erth with a krash and land on Hal.

1. _____	4. _____	7. _____
2. _____	5. _____	8. _____
3. _____	6. _____	9. _____

Word Bank

crash	hatch	neck	rush	splash
earth	kick	porch	sack	switch
fresh	match	ranch	sandwich	teacher

G Dictation

Name _____

Listen **and** write the missing words and punctuation.

1. _____ _____ _____ _____ _____

_____ Tommy's bike_

2. Tommy _____ _____ _____ _____ _____

_____ _____ _

3. _____ _____ _____ drive _____ _____ _____

_____ _____ _____ _____

H Proofreading

If a word is misspelled, fill in the oval by that word. If all the words are spelled correctly, fill in the oval by **no mistake**.

1. ⚬ bump
   ⚬ fresh
   ⚬ crash
   ⚬ no mistake

4. ⚬ rush
   ⚬ kik
   ⚬ young
   ⚬ no mistake

7. ⚬ aunt
   ⚬ behind
   ⚬ sak
   ⚬ no mistake

2. ⚬ erth
   ⚬ neck
   ⚬ front
   ⚬ no mistake

5. ⚬ splash
   ⚬ macth
   ⚬ husband
   ⚬ no mistake

8. ⚬ sanwhich
   ⚬ butter
   ⚬ address
   ⚬ no mistake

3. ⚬ porch
   ⚬ stamp
   ⚬ hach
   ⚬ no mistake

6. ⚬ rantch
   ⚬ drank
   ⚬ grandfather
   ⚬ no mistake

9. ⚬ spend
   ⚬ teecher
   ⚬ string
   ⚬ no mistake

I Game

Name _____

Complete the secret phrase by correctly spelling the words from this week's word list.

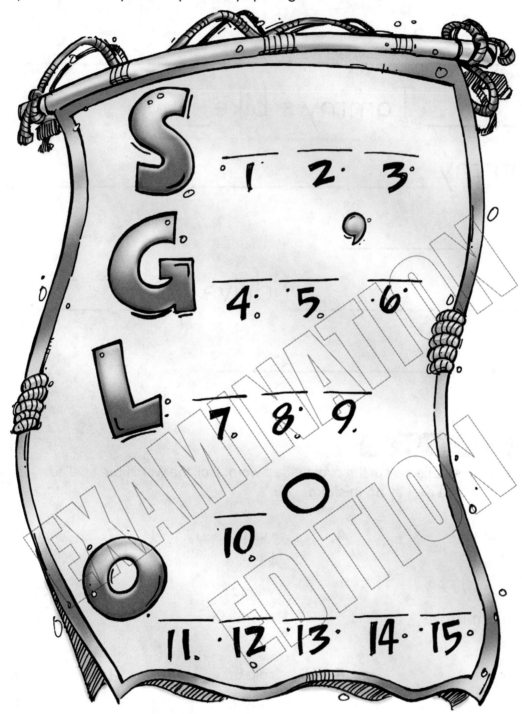

S $\overline{}$ $\overline{}$ $\overline{}$
  1   2   3

      ,
      9

G $\overline{}$
  4   5   6

L $\overline{}$
  7 8 9

  $\overline{}$ O
  10

O $\overline{}$
  11 12 13 14 15

Remember: Love can cover many flaws!

J Journaling

In your journal, make a list of people you know. Then write a prayer asking God to help you show deep love for each person on the list.

A Preview

Write each word as your teacher says it.

Name _____

1. _____

2. _____

3. _____

4. _____

5. _____

6. _____

7. _____

8. _____

9. _____

10. _____

11. _____

12. _____

13. _____

14. _____

15. _____

Scripture

1 Peter 4:10

Write each word in the correct word shape boxes. Next, in the word shape boxes, color the silent consonant or consonants in each word. Circle the word in which the digraph **wh** has the sound of **/h/**.

1. bright
2. caught
3. chalk
4. clothes
5. half
6. knee
7. knot
8. neighbor
9. sidewalk
10. sight
11. though
12. thumb
13. Wednesday
14. whole
15. wrap

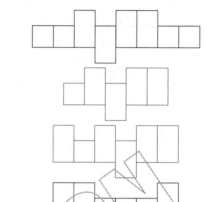
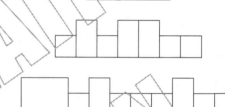
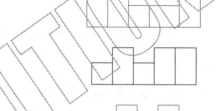
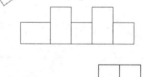
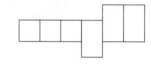
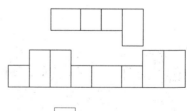
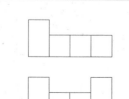

C Hide and Seek

Name _____

Place an **X** on a coin for each word you spell correctly.

D Other Word Forms

Using the words below, follow the instructions given by your teacher.

although	clothing	knotted	thumbs
brighten	halftime	knotting	wholesome
brightest	halfway	neighborly	wholly
catch	halved	sidewalks	wrapped
catches	halves	sighted	wrapping
catching	knees	sights	wraps
chalky	knots	thumbed	

E Fun Ways to Spell

Initial the box of each activity you finish.

1.

Spell your words with markers.

3.

Spell your words while snapping.

2.

Spell your words with letter tiles.

4.

Spell your words with paint.

F **Working with Words**

Name _____

Spelling Clues

Write the words in which you see the letter **l** but don't hear **/l/**.

1. _____   2. _____   3. _____

Write the words in which you see the letter **k** but don't hear **/k/**.

4. _____   5. _____

Write the words in which you see the letter **w** but don't hear **/w/**.

6. _____   7. _____

Write the words in which you see the letters **g** and **h** but don't hear **/g/** or **/h/**.

8. _____   9. _____   10. _____

11. _____   12. _____

Which word has the consonant digraph **th** that is silent?

13. _____

Write the word in which you see the letter **b**, but don't hear **/b/**.

14. _____

Write the word in which you see the letter **d**, but don't hear **/d/**.

15. _____

Missing Letters

Write the consonant digraph for these spelling words.

1. ___ ___ ot   2. ___ ___ ap   3. ___ ___ umb

4. ___ ___ ee   5. ___ ___ ole   6. ___ ___ ough

Word Bank

bright	clothes	knot	sight	Wednesday
caught	half	neighbor	though	whole
chalk	knee	sidewalk	thumb	wrap

G Dictation

Name _____

Listen and write the missing words and punctuation.

1. Tony ____ _____ ____ ____

   " " _____ ____ ____ __

2. Mr. Valentino ____ ____ ____

   __ ____ __

3. Matthew ____ ____ ____ ____

   touch ____ _____

H Proofreading

If a word is misspelled, fill in the oval by that word. If all the words are spelled correctly, fill in the oval by **no mistake**.

1. ◯ knot
   ◯ earth
   ◯ brite
   ◯ no mistake

2. ◯ sight
   ◯ hatch
   ◯ chaulk
   ◯ no mistake

3. ◯ caut
   ◯ kick
   ◯ sack
   ◯ no mistake

4. ◯ clothz
   ◯ thumb
   ◯ sandwich
   ◯ no mistake

5. ◯ whole
   ◯ teacher
   ◯ haf
   ◯ no mistake

6. ◯ wrap
   ◯ knea
   ◯ ranch
   ◯ no mistake

7. ◯ negbor
   ◯ sidewalk
   ◯ match
   ◯ no mistake

8. ◯ ink
   ◯ wind
   ◯ though
   ◯ no mistake

9. ◯ Wensday
   ◯ scrub
   ◯ scream
   ◯ no mistake

71

I | Game

Glue on a piece of the puzzle-picture for each word you or your team spells correctly from this week's word list.

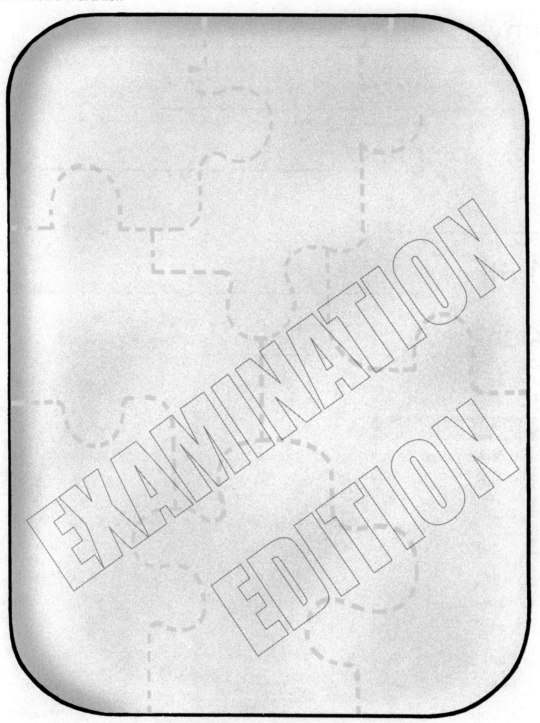

Remember: Use the gifts God has given you to bless someone else.

J | Journaling

In your journal, write about how you can use one of your special abilities to help someone you know.

Name _____

Write each spelling word on the line as your teacher says it.

1. _____

2. _____

3. _____

4. _____

5. _____

6. _____

7. _____

8. _____

9. _____

10. _____

11. _____

12. _____

B **Test-Sentences**

Write the sentences on the lines below, correcting each misspelled word, as well as all capitalization and punctuation errors. There are two misspelled words in each sentence.

the sidewak on our streat is badly cracked?

1. _____

Flip the swich if you need some brite light

2. _____

is your aunte riding with your granmother.

3. _____

73

C Test-Dictation

Name _____

Listen and write the missing words and punctuation.

1. _____ _____ climbed _____ _____ _____ _____ _____

2. _____ _____ likes _____ _____ _____ _____ _____ _____

3. _____ _____ outside _____ _____ _____ _____

_____ _____ _____ _____

4. _____ _____ _____ _____ _____ deck _____ _____

_____ _____ _____

D Test-Proofreading

If a word is misspelled, fill in the oval by that word. If all the words are spelled correctly, fill in the oval by **no mistake**.

1. ○ screem
   ○ lesson
   ○ bright
   ○ no mistake

2. ○ spring
   ○ husband
   ○ thumb
   ○ no mistake

3. ○ porch
   ○ kick
   ○ straw
   ○ no mistake

4. ○ million
   ○ knee
   ○ streem
   ○ no mistake

5. ○ suddin
   ○ classroom
   ○ fresh
   ○ no mistake

6. ○ drank
   ○ front
   ○ ranch
   ○ no mistake

7. ○ neighbor
   ○ yung
   ○ threw
   ○ no mistake

8. ○ chalk
   ○ ink
   ○ macth
   ○ no mistake

9. ○ butter
   ○ erth
   ○ half
   ○ no mistake

E Test-Shapes

If a word is misspelled, color the tire or tube by that word.

thum

strong

wing

reelly

half

happin

nee

bump

clothez

beelong

splash

string

neck

merrey

F Writing Assessment

Write a paragraph about a time you were lonely like Tommy. Remember to tell when it happened, for whom you were lonely, why you were lonely, where you were, and how you got to feeling better. Don't forget that the Lord is listening to your prayers.

_____

_____

_____

_____

_____

_____

_____

Scripture

I Peter 3:12

Write the sentences on the lines below, correcting each misspelled word, as well as all capitalization and punctuation errors. There are two misspelled words in each sentence.

Put a stapm on the letter to your granfather

1. _____

they sagn that tune in frunt of their class

2. _____

Our nayber bought a huge rantch.

3. _____

H **Test-Words**

Write each spelling word on the line as your teacher says it.

1. _____ 7. _____

2. _____ 8. _____

3. _____ 9. _____

4. _____ 10. _____

5. _____ 11. _____

6. _____ 12. _____

Review

Lesson

12

Name _____

If a word is spelled correctly, fill in the oval under **Correct**. If the word is misspelled, fill in the oval under **Incorrect**, and spell the word correctly on the blank.

Correct   Incorrect

1. skrap   ⬭   ⬭   _____

2. straight   ⬭   ⬭   _____

3. buter   ⬭   ⬭   _____

4. milloin   ⬭   ⬭   _____

5. rubber   ⬭   ⬭   _____

6. behind   ⬭   ⬭   _____

7. wind   ⬭   ⬭   _____

8. hach   ⬭   ⬭   _____

9. sak   ⬭   ⬭   _____

10. caut   ⬭   ⬭   _____

11. knot   ⬭   ⬭   _____

12. tho   ⬭   ⬭   _____

Review

Lesson

12

Name _____

Score points for each review word or Other Word Form you or your team spells correctly.

Remember: God is always ready to hear what you have to say.

Spelling Is Fun!

This certificate is awarded to

_____

for practicing the following words, by doing terrific
spelling activities, and playing great spelling games!

Date _____

A Reason For SPELLING

scrap	address	aunt	crash	bright
scratch	butter	behind	earth	caught
scream	classroom	belong	fresh	chalk
screen	happen	bump	hatch	clothes
scrub	ladder	drank	kick	half
spread	lesson	front	match	knee
spring	merry	grandfather	neck	knot
straight	million	grandmother	porch	neighbor
strange	really	husband	ranch	sidewalk
straw	rubber	ink	rush	sight
stream	smell	sang	sack	though
street	sudden	stamp	sandwich	thumb
string	sunny	wind	splash	Wednesday
strong	supper	wing	switch	whole
threw	unhappy	young	teacher	wrap

Dear Parent,

We are about to begin a new spelling unit containing five weekly lessons. A set of fifteen words will be studied each week. All the words will be reviewed in the sixth week. Values based on the Scriptures listed below will be taught in each lesson.

Lesson 13	Lesson 14	Lesson 15	Lesson 16	Lesson 17
angel	asleep	careful	afraid	angry
cage	boss	copy	awake	busy
edge	certain	cover	date	carry
giraffe	circus	fork	eight	creek
huge	gas	kept	lady	deep
January	less	key	lay	February
jar	pass	October	made	field
jealous	race	queen	mail	heavy
jolly	save	quick	paper	honey
judge	sell	quiet	plane	leave
jug	seventh	quilt	sail	marry
juice	since	quite	shade	meal
July	soap	rack	table	mean
June	sorry	rake	wait	team
rage	sweet	track	weigh	twenty

1 Peter 3:4	1 Peter 3:8	1 John 1:7	1 Peter 3:9	Ephesians 3:17

Write each word as your teacher says it.

1. _____

2. _____

3. _____

4. _____

5. _____

6. _____

7. _____

8. _____

9. _____

10. _____

11. _____

Words with /j/

Lesson

13

12. _____

13. _____

14. _____

15. _____

Scripture

1 Peter 3:4

Name _____

Write each word in the correct word shape boxes. Next, in the word shape boxes, color the letter or letters that spell the sound of **/j/** in each word. Circle the words in which **/j/** is spelled **dg**.

1. angel

2. cage

3. edge

4. giraffe

5. huge

6. January

7. jar

8. jealous

9. jolly

10. judge

11. jug

12. juice

13. July

14. June

15. rage

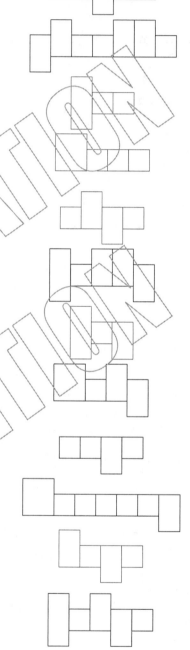

C Hide and Seek

Name _____

Place an **X** on a coin for each word you spell correctly.

D Other Word Forms

Using the words below, follow the instructions given by your teacher.

angelic	hugely	jolliest	juicily
angels	hugeness	judged	juiciness
caged	jarred	judging	juicy
cages	jarring	judgment	raged
cagey	jars	judgmental	raging
edges	jealously	judicial	
edging	jealousy	jugs	
giraffes	jollier	juicier	

E Fun Ways to Spell

Initial the box of each activity you finish.

1.

Spell your words with puzzles.

2.

Spell your words with stencils.

3.

Spell your words in rhythm.

4.

Spell your words with play dough.

Name _____

Rhyming Words

Write the spelling word or words that rhyme with the words below.

Words with /j/

Lesson

13

stage   holly   soon

1. _____   2. _____   3. _____

fudge   zealous   shrug

4. _____   5. _____   6. _____

ledge   far   loose

7. _____   8. _____   9. _____

Clues

Write the spelling word that matches each clue.

1. first month _____   8. a heavenly messenger _____

2. an African mammal _____ 9. very large _____

3. seventh month _____   10. place for an animal _____

4. sixth month _____   11. a glass container _____

5. envious _____   12. full of high spirits _____

6. a small pitcher _____   13. a public official _____

7. liquid from a fruit _____ 14. violent anger _____

Dictionary Skills

A dictionary entry word is followed by a definition. A definition tells what the word means. Write the spelling word that would be the entry word for each definition below.

1. _____ a container made of wires in which animals are kept

2. _____ the sharp side of a cutting tool

Word Bank

angel	giraffe	jar	judge	July
cage	huge	jealous	jug	June
edge	January	jolly	juice	rage

84

G Dictation

Name _____

Listen and write the missing words and punctuation.

1. _____ ___ _____ ___ _____ ___

   _____ _____ __

2. Rosa _____ ___ sun-catcher ___ ___

   ____ _____ __

3. Rosa learned ___ _____ _____

   ___ ___ _____ _____

H Proofreading

If a word is misspelled, fill in the oval by that word. If all the words are spelled correctly, fill in the oval by **no mistake**.

1. ○ huge
   ○ aengle
   ○ bright
   ○ no mistake

2. ○ half
   ○ chalk
   ○ caje
   ○ no mistake

3. ○ edg
   ○ jar
   ○ jolly
   ○ no mistake

4. ○ jiraffe
   ○ caught
   ○ clothes
   ○ no mistake

5. ○ jug
   ○ knee
   ○ Janary
   ○ no mistake

6. ○ Wednesday
   ○ June
   ○ jelous
   ○ no mistake

7. ○ neighbor
   ○ rage
   ○ juge
   ○ no mistake

8. ○ juce
   ○ neck
   ○ splash
   ○ no mistake

9. ○ knot
   ○ rush
   ○ july
   ○ no mistake

I Game

Name _____

Mr. Valentino's class is visiting the people who live at the Pleasant Valley Retirement Home. Lead the way by moving one space for each word you or your team spells correctly from this week's word list.

Remember: God looks inside you to see who you really are.

J Journaling

In your journal, list as many character traits as you can think of that help to make a person beautiful inside. Circle a character trait that a friend has and write about how you see that good trait in his or her life.

Name _____

Write each word as your teacher says it.

1. _____

2. _____

3. _____

4. _____

5. _____

6. _____

7. _____

8. _____

9. _____

10. _____

11. _____

12. _____

13. _____

14. _____

15. _____

Scripture

I Peter 3:8

Write each word in the correct word shape boxes. Next, in the word shape boxes, color the letter or letters that spell the sound of **/s/** in each word. Circle the words in which **/s/** is spelled with both **s** and **c**.

1. asleep

2. boss

3. certain

4. circus

5. gas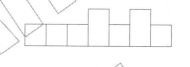

6. less

7. pass

8. race

9. save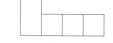

10. sell

11. seventh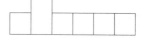

12. since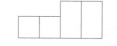

13. soap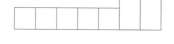

14. sorry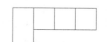

15. sweet

C Hide and Seek

Place an **X** on a coin for each word you spell correctly.

D Other Word Forms

Using the words below, follow the instructions given by your teacher.

bossily	gassing	racism	sleeping
bossiness	lessen	saved	sleepy
bossing	lesser	saving	soapy
bossy	passable	savings	sorrier
certainly	passes	selling	sorriest
certainty	passing	sold	sorrow
circuses	raced	seven	sweeten
gases	racially	sleepily	sweetly
gasoline	racing	sleepiness	sweetness

E Fun Ways to Spell

Initial the box of each activity you finish.

1. ☐

Spell your words with chalk.

3. ☐

Spell your words out of the letter box.

2. ☐

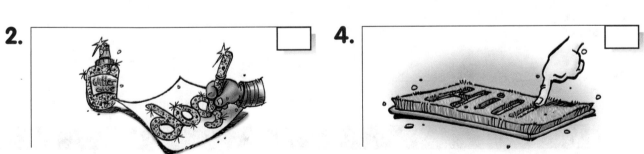

Spell your words with glitter glue.

4. ☐

Spell your words on carpet.

89

Name _____

Spelling Clues

Words in which **c** has the sound of **/s/** usually have the letter **e**, **i**, or **y** following the **c**. Write the words in which **/s/** is spelled with **c**. Now, circle the vowel that comes after each **c** with the sound of **/s/**.

1. _____   3. _____

2. _____   4. _____

ABC Order

Write the words from each group in alphabetical order.

| less | pass | boss |

1. _____   2. _____   3. _____

| asleep | race | gas |

4. _____   5. _____   6. _____

Remember, when words begin with the same letter, look at the second letter to place the words in alphabetical order.

| circus | since | certain |

7. _____   8. _____   9. _____

| seventh | sweet | save |

10. _____   11. _____   12. _____

Remember, if the first two letters are the same, look at the third letter to place the words in alphabetical order.

| sorry | sell | soap |

13. _____   14. _____   15. _____

Word Bank

certain	asleep	less	seventh	sorry
circus	boss	pass	sell	sweet
race	gas	save	soap	since

G Dictation

Name _____

Listen and write the missing words and punctuation.

1. Helen _____ _____ _____ Rachel

_____ _____ _____ _

2. Mr. Valentino _____ __ _____ _____

___ papers_

3. Daniel _____ _____ paper _____ _

_____ pack __ _____ _

H Proofreading

If a word is misspelled, fill in the oval by that word. If all the words are spelled correctly, fill in the oval by **no mistake**.

1.
- ○ angel
- ○ asleap
- ○ boss
- ○ no mistake

4.
- ○ race
- ○ juice
- ○ gass
- ○ no mistake

7.
- ○ saop
- ○ jealous
- ○ January
- ○ no mistake

2.
- ○ certun
- ○ cage
- ○ less
- ○ no mistake

5.
- ○ sevinth
- ○ save
- ○ judge
- ○ no mistake

8.
- ○ though
- ○ sight
- ○ sorrie
- ○ no mistake

3.
- ○ July
- ○ circuss
- ○ pass
- ○ no mistake

6.
- ○ giraffe
- ○ sinse
- ○ sell
- ○ no mistake

9.
- ○ wrap
- ○ sweet
- ○ sidewalk
- ○ no mistake

I Game

Mr. Valentino is passing out the lists of the special qualities his students wrote about each other. Lead the way by moving one space for each word you or your team spells correctly from this week's word list.

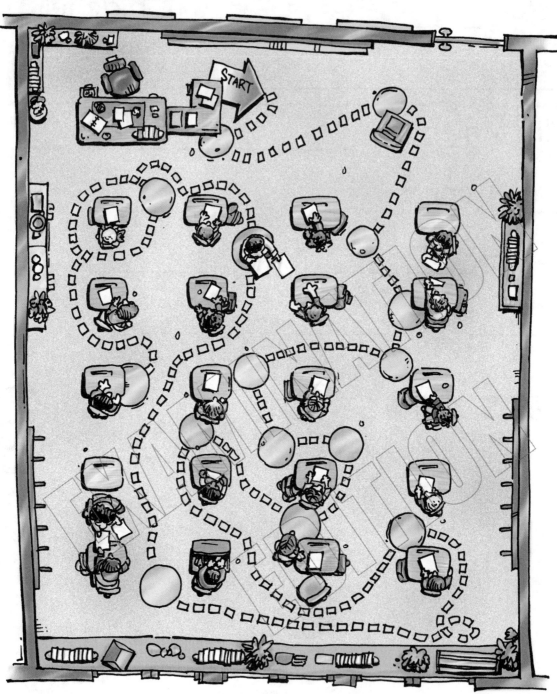

Remember: Getting along with each other is the result of walking with God.

J Journaling

In your journal, make a list of all the students in your class. Write the nicest thing you can say about each one.

A Preview

Write each word as your teacher says it.

Name _____

1. _____

2. _____

3. _____

4. _____

5. _____

6. _____

7. _____

8. _____

9. _____

10. _____

11. _____

12. _____

13. _____

14. _____

15. _____

Scripture

I John 1:7

Name _____

Write each word in the correct word shape boxes. Next, in the word shape boxes, color the letter or letters that spell the sound of **/k/** or **/kw/** in each word.

1. careful

2. copy

3. cover

4. fork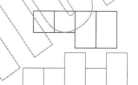

5. kept

6. key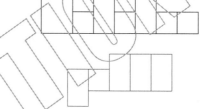

7. October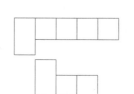

8. queen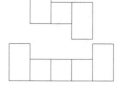

9. quick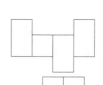

10. quiet

11. quilt

12. quite

13. rack

14. rake

15. track

C Hide and Seek

Name _____

Place an **X** on a coin for each word you spell correctly.

D Other Word Forms

Using the words below, follow the instructions given by your teacher.

carefully	covering	queenly	racket
carefulness	forked	quicken	raked
copier	keep	quickly	raking
copies	keeping	quietly	tracked
coverage	keyed	quietness	tracking
covered	keys	quilted	tracks

E Fun Ways to Spell

Initial the box of each activity you finish.

1. ☐

Spell your words with pictures.

3. ☐

Spell your words out loud.

2. ☐

Spell your words with lemon juice.

4. ☐

Spell your words with pipe cleaners.

95

Name _____

Crossword Puzzle

Use the clues to write the words in the puzzle.

Across

2. a fall month
5. unlocks a door
6. used to eat with
9. a padded bed cover
10. a path used for trains
14. completely
15. calm and peaceful

Down

1. imitate
3. using caution
4. frame to put things on
7. took care of
8. fast, speedy
11. garden tool
12. to place something over
13. wife of a king

Word Bank

careful	fork	October	quiet	rack
copy	kept	queen	quilt	rake
cover	key	quick	quite	track

G Dictation

Listen and write the missing words and punctuation.

1. Rebecca ____ ____ ____ ____

   ____ ____ __

2. Rachel ____ ____ ____ ____

   heartbeat __ __ ____ __

3. Rachel ____ ____ ____ ____

   verse neatly__

H Proofreading

If a word is misspelled, fill in the oval by that word. If all the words are spelled correctly, fill in the oval by **no mistake**.

1. ◯ certain
   ◯ carefull
   ◯ asleep
   ◯ no mistake

4. ◯ quick
   ◯ kee
   ◯ gas
   ◯ no mistake

7. ◯ since
   ◯ queit
   ◯ soap
   ◯ no mistake

2. ◯ fork
   ◯ June
   ◯ copie
   ◯ no mistake

5. ◯ seventh
   ◯ quilt
   ◯ october
   ◯ no mistake

8. ◯ race
   ◯ rack
   ◯ sorry
   ◯ no mistake

3. ◯ cuver
   ◯ circus
   ◯ kept
   ◯ no mistake

6. ◯ quean
   ◯ quite
   ◯ rake
   ◯ no mistake

9. ◯ jar
   ◯ rage
   ◯ trak
   ◯ no mistake

I Game

Fill in the secret phrase by correctly spelling the words from this week's word list.

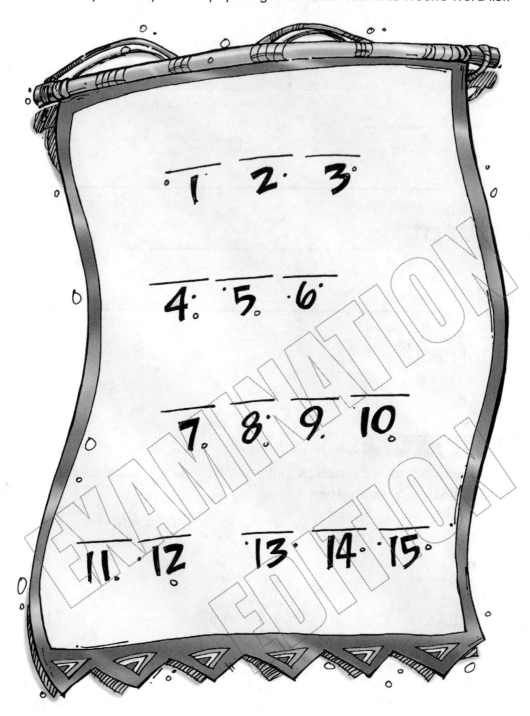

Remember: Walk in God's light and have great fellowship with others.

J Journaling

In your journal, make a list of at least 5 people with whom you have a wonderful time. Write a letter to one of them and tell them why you enjoy their company.

A Preview

Write each word as your teacher says it.

Name _____

1. _____

2. _____

3. _____

4. _____

5. _____

6. _____

7. _____

8. _____

9. _____

10. _____

11. _____

12. _____

13. _____

14. _____

15. _____

Scripture

I Peter 3:9

Name _____

Write each word in the correct word shape boxes. Next, in the word shape boxes, color the letter or letters that spell the sound of /ā/ in each word. Circle the words in which /ā/ is spelled **ei**.

1. afraid

2. awake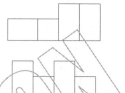

3. date

4. eight

5. lady

6. lay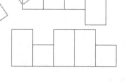

7. made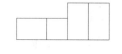

8. mail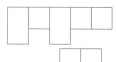

9. paper

10. plane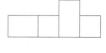

11. sail

12. shade

13. table

14. wait

15. weigh

C Hide and Seek

Name _____

Place an **X** on a coin for each word you spell correctly.

D Other Word Forms

Using the words below, follow the instructions given by your teacher.

awakened	ladies	making	sailor	waited
awakening	laid	papery	shaded	waiter
awoke	laying	planed	shading	waiting
dated	mailed	planer	shady	waitress
dates	mailing	planing	tabled	weight
dating	mails	sailed	tabletop	weightless
eighth	make	sailing	tableware	weighty

E Fun Ways to Spell

Initial the box of each activity you finish.

1. ☐

Spell your words in your classmate's hand.

3. ☐

Spell your words using a tape recorder.

2. ☐

Spell your words with paper cups.

4. ☐

Spell your words with magazine clippings.

101

F Working with Words

Name _____

Sentence Fun

Write the correct spelling word on the line to complete each sentence.

1. A woman is called a _____.

2. A tree gives _____ from the sun.

3. The squares on a calendar mark the _____.

4. To set something down is to _____ it down.

5. The opposite of asleep is _____.

6. Filled with fear means _____.

7. We eat at the _____.

8. You use a scale to see how much you _____.

9. The number after seven is _____.

10. To send a letter is to _____ it.

11. Formed or prepared means _____.

12. Ocean is to boat as air is to _____.

13. We write on _____.

14. Wind blows on the _____ to move a boat.

15. The opposite of hurry is _____.

Spelling Clues

Which words have the same spelling of /ā/ as neighbor?

16. _____ 17. _____

Write the spelling words that rhyme with state.

18. _____ 19. _____ 20. _____

Word Bank

afraid	eight	made	plane	table
awake	lady	mail	sail	wait
date	lay	paper	shade	weigh

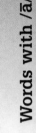

G Dictation

Name _____

Listen and write the missing words and punctuation.

1. Stephen watched Christopher ____ ____

____ ____ ____ ____ ____ _

2. Daniel ___ _____ Christopher ____

blame ____ _

3. Christopher ____ _____ _____

____ ____ ____ _

H Proofreading

If a word is misspelled, fill in the oval by that word. If all the words are spelled correctly, fill in the oval by **no mistake**.

1.
- ⬭ afrade
- ⬭ awake
- ⬭ careful
- ⬭ no mistake

2.
- ⬭ copy
- ⬭ cover
- ⬭ daet
- ⬭ no mistake

3.
- ⬭ eite
- ⬭ key
- ⬭ October
- ⬭ no mistake

4.
- ⬭ lay
- ⬭ mail
- ⬭ ladie
- ⬭ no mistake

5.
- ⬭ maide
- ⬭ paper
- ⬭ queen
- ⬭ no mistake

6.
- ⬭ plaene
- ⬭ wait
- ⬭ quiet
- ⬭ no mistake

7.
- ⬭ track
- ⬭ sial
- ⬭ weigh
- ⬭ no mistake

8.
- ⬭ shade
- ⬭ sweet
- ⬭ save
- ⬭ no mistake

9.
- ⬭ fork
- ⬭ quilt
- ⬭ tabel
- ⬭ no mistake

I | Game

Glue on a piece of the puzzle-picture for each word you or your team spells correctly from this week's word list.

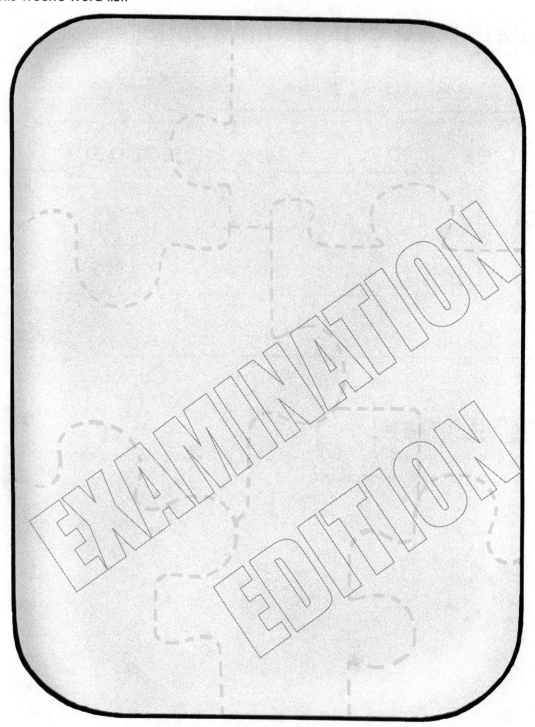

Remember: God will bless you for being kind to the unkind.

J | Journaling

Decide whether you are going to write from Christopher's or Daniel's view point. In your journal, write about what happened in this story as if you were Christopher or Daniel.

A Preview

Write each word as your teacher says it.

Name _____

1. _____

2. _____

3. _____

4. _____

5. _____

6. _____

7. _____

8. _____

9. _____

10. _____

11. _____

12. _____

13. _____

14. _____

15. _____

Scripture

Ephesians 3:17

Name _____

Write each word in the correct word shape boxes. Next, in the word shape boxes, color the letter or letters that spell the sound of /ē/ in each word. Circle the words with more than one syllable.

1. angry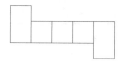

2. busy

3. carry

4. creek

5. deep

6. February

7. field

8. heavy

9. honey

10. leave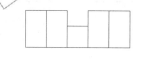

11. marry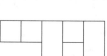

12. meal

13. mean

14. team

15. twenty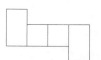

C Hide and Seek

Name _____

Place an **X** on a coin for each word you spell correctly.

D Other Word Forms

Using the words below, follow the instructions given by your teacher.

angrier	carrying	heaviness	marrying
angriest	deepen	honeys	mealy
angrily	deeply	leaving	meaning
busied	fielder	leavings	meaningful
busier	heavier	left	meanly
busiest	heaviest	married	meanness
carried	heavily	marries	teaming

E Fun Ways to Spell

Initial the box of each activity you finish.

1.

Spell your words with markers.

3.

Spell your words while snapping.

2.

Spell your words with letter tiles.

4.

Spell your words with paint.

Proofing

Use proofreader's marks to show the errors in the paragraph below. Write the misspelled words correctly on the lines.

⬭ word is misspelled	⋀ word or words missing	☰ capitalize letter

The hevy, febuwary rains made creak very depe. The angree water rushed fast enough to cerry tree limbs and other rubbish. It kept a teem of twinty men bisy trying to rescue the calves were trapped the high corner of the feeld. then we all down to enjoy hot meel.

1. _____   5. _____   9. _____

2. _____   6. _____   10. _____

3. _____   7. _____   11. _____

4. _____   8. _____

Dictionary Skills

A dictionary definition tells what an entry word means. Sometimes a **sample sentence** comes after the definition. The entry word is in the sentence to help you understand the word meaning. Write a sample sentence for the entry words below.

mean. To matter: My friends mean a lot to me.
The sample sentence is: My friends mean a lot to me.

honey

1. _____

leave

2. _____

Word Bank

angry	creek	field	leave	mean
busy	deep	heavy	marry	team
carry	February	honey	meal	twenty

G Dictation

Name _____

Listen and write the missing words and punctuation.

1. Setsuko ____ _____ ___ _____

___ _____ _

2. Mrs. Noma ___ _____ ___ _____

___ Setsuko _

3. Setsuko ____ _____ ___ _____

minutes ____ _____ ___ _

H Proofreading

If a word is misspelled, fill in the oval by that word. If all the words are spelled correctly, fill in the oval by **no mistake**.

1. ◯ angry
   ◯ buzy
   ◯ afraid
   ◯ no mistake

2. ◯ date
   ◯ eight
   ◯ cary
   ◯ no mistake

3. ◯ creke
   ◯ lady
   ◯ honey
   ◯ no mistake

4. ◯ made
   ◯ deap
   ◯ plane
   ◯ no mistake

5. ◯ february
   ◯ sail
   ◯ mean
   ◯ no mistake

6. ◯ team
   ◯ feild
   ◯ table
   ◯ no mistake

7. ◯ hevy
   ◯ twenty
   ◯ quick
   ◯ no mistake

8. ◯ leave
   ◯ marry
   ◯ wait
   ◯ no mistake

9. ◯ meal
   ◯ mail
   ◯ paper
   ◯ no mistake

I Game

Andrea needs to check on Setsuko who is resting in her room. Lead the way by moving one space for each word you or your team spells correctly from this week's word list.

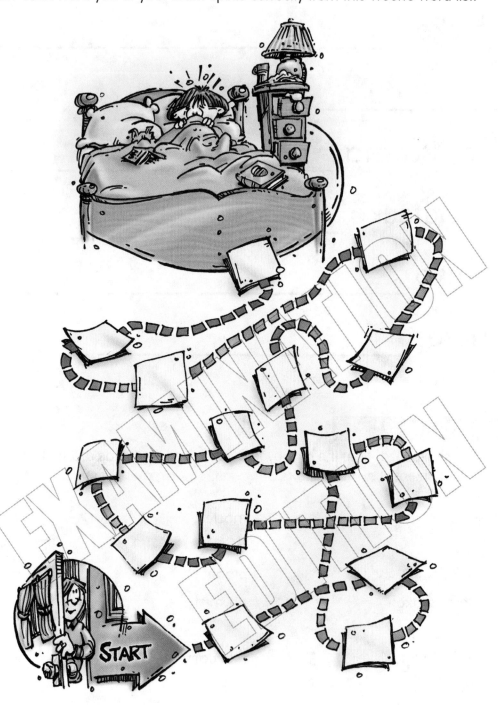

Remember: Allow Jesus to be your closest Friend. Trust Him always.

J Journaling

In your journal, write about a time when you were afraid. Tell how having Christ at home in your heart can help you when you're afraid.

A Test-Words

Write each spelling word on the line as your teacher says it.

Name _____

1. _____

2. _____

3. _____

4. _____

5. _____

6. _____

7. _____

8. _____

9. _____

10. _____

11. _____

12. _____

B Test-Sentences

Write the sentences on the lines below, correcting each misspelled word, as well as all capitalization and punctuation errors. There are two misspelled words in each sentence.

please saev the sevinth seat for me?

1. _____

This sope has a very swete smell

2. _____

The kwean gave the little girl a gold kee.

3. _____

C Test-Dictation

Name _____

Listen and write the missing words and punctuation.

1. _____ _____ _____ _____ _____ laugh_

2. _____ _____ _____ _____ _____ _____ _

3. _____ _____ _____ _____ leaves

_____ _____ _

4. _____ _____ _____ _____ early

_____ morning_

Review

Lesson

18

D Test-Proofreading

If a word is misspelled, fill in the oval by that word. If all the words are spelled correctly, fill in the oval by **no mistake**.

1. ◯ race
   ◯ edje
   ◯ asleep
   ◯ no mistake

2. ◯ jellus
   ◯ pass
   ◯ paper
   ◯ no mistake

3. ◯ boss
   ◯ certain
   ◯ mean
   ◯ no mistake

4. ◯ sinse
   ◯ eight
   ◯ honey
   ◯ no mistake

5. ◯ fork
   ◯ gas
   ◯ shade
   ◯ no mistake

6. ◯ mail
   ◯ creek
   ◯ quik
   ◯ no mistake

7. ◯ rack
   ◯ busy
   ◯ February
   ◯ no mistake

8. ◯ plane
   ◯ field
   ◯ key
   ◯ no mistake

9. ◯ deap
   ◯ team
   ◯ huge
   ◯ no mistake

E Test-Shapes

Name _____

If a word is misspelled, color the rice bowl by that word.

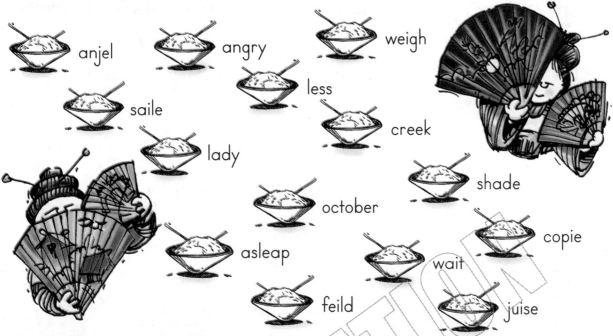

anjel

angry

weigh

saile

less

creek

lady

october

shade

asleap

wait

copie

feild

juise

F Writing Assessment

Write a letter to God telling Him how you feel about obeying. Ask Him to work in your life to help you do what He wants you to do.

_____

_____

_____

_____

_____

_____

_____

_____

Scripture

Philippians 2:13

G Test-Sentences

Name _____

Write the sentences on the lines below, correcting each misspelled word, as well as all capitalization and punctuation errors. There are two misspelled words in each sentence.

Mom is serten the sirkus is coming to town.

1. _____

my birthday is in januairy, not in july

2. _____

The jiraffe at the zoo is not in a caje.

3. _____

H Test-Words

Write each spelling word on the line as your teacher says it.

1. _____   7. _____

2. _____   8. _____

3. _____   9. _____

4. _____   10. _____

5. _____   11. _____

6. _____   12. _____

Name _____

If a word is spelled correctly, fill in the oval under **Correct**. If the word is misspelled, fill in the oval under **Incorrect**, and spell the word correctly on the blank.

		Correct	Incorrect	
1.	judg	○	○	_____
2.	jug	○	○	_____
3.	June	○	○	_____
4.	raje	○	○	_____
5.	race	○	○	_____
6.	sel	○	○	_____
7.	kwite	○	○	_____
8.	trac	○	○	_____
9.	Febuary	○	○	_____
10.	honey	○	○	_____
11.	marrie	○	○	_____
12.	team	○	○	_____

Score points for each review word or Other Word Form you or your team spells correctly.

Remember: God will help you desire to obey Him.

Spelling Is Fun!

ABC's

This certificate is awarded to

_____

for practicing the following words, by doing terrific
spelling activities, and playing great spelling games!

Date _____

angel	asleep	careful	afraid	angry
cage	boss	copy	awake	busy
edge	certain	cover	date	carry
giraffe	circus	fork	eight	creek
huge	gas	kept	lady	deep
January	less	key	lay	February
jar	pass	October	made	field
jealous	race	queen	mail	heavy
jolly	save	quick	paper	honey
judge	sell	quiet	plane	leave
jug	seventh	quilt	sail	marry
juice	since	quite	shade	meal
July	soap	rack	table	mean
June	sorry	rake	wait	team
rage	sweet	track	weigh	twenty

A Reason For Spelling®

Dear Parent,

   We are about to begin a new spelling unit containing five weekly lessons. A set of fifteen words will be studied each week. All the words will be reviewed in the sixth week. Values based on the Scriptures listed below will be taught in each lesson.

Lesson 19	Lesson 20	Lesson 21	Lesson 22	Lesson 23
bicycle	ago	August	allow	airport
die	alone	autumn	amount	corner
fight	float	bought	anyhow	course
Friday	follow	brought	clown	floor
lie	goes	cause	crowd	fort
life	gold	daughter	doubt	fourth
nearby	open	fought	drown	horn
ripe	owe	hall	ground	order
shy	rode	paw	hour	pour
sign	rope	raw	loud	report
smile	sew	salt	mouse	score
tight	shown	song	mouth	sore
tiny	spoke	taught	plow	sport
wild	telephone	upon	power	storm
wipe	toast	wall	shout	wore

Philippians 1:11   Colossians 3:13   Colossians 3:14   James 3:17   Ephesians 4:2

A Preview

Write each word as your teacher says it.

1. _____

2. _____

3. _____

4. _____

5. _____

6. _____

7. _____

8. _____

9. _____

10. _____

11. _____

12. _____

13. _____

14. _____

15. _____

May you always be doing those good, kind things which show that you are a child of God, for this will bring much praise and glory to the Lord.

Scripture

Philippians 1:11

Name _____

Write each word in the correct word shape boxes. Next, in the word shape boxes, color the letter or letters that spell the sound of /ī/ in each word. Circle the words which have the silent consonants **gh**.

1. bicycle

2. die

3. fight

4. Friday

5. lie

6. life

7. nearby

8. ripe

9. shy

10. sign

11. smile

12. tight

13. tiny

14. wild

15. wipe

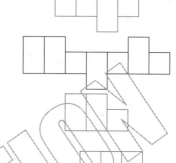
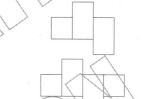
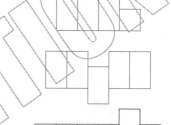
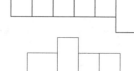
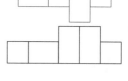
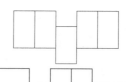
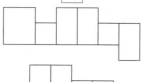

C Hide and Seek

Name _____

Place an **X** on a coin for each word you spell correctly.

D Other Word Forms

Using the words below, follow the instructions given by your teacher.

bicycled	lay	ripen	signal	tiniest
bicycling	lied	ripened	signed	wilderness
bicyclist	lying	ripening	signing	wildly
died	lifeless	riper	smiled	wildness
dying	lifelike	ripest	smiling	wiped
fighter	lives	shied	tighten	wiper
fighting	near	shying	tightly	wiping
fought	nearly	shyly	tightness	
lain	nearness	shyness	tinier	

E Fun Ways to Spell

Initial the box of each activity you finish.

1. ☐

Spell your words with puzzles.

3. ☐

Spell your words in rhythm.

2. ☐

Spell your words with stencils.

4. ☐

Spell your words with play dough.

Name _____

Secret Words

Use the clues to write the words in the puzzle. Then write the boxed letters on the lines below and find the words from this week's Scripture.

1. very little
2. close to you
3. a happy look on your face
4. two-wheeled vehicle with pedals
5. bashful
6. not the truth
7. alive
8. not tame
9. battle
10. symbol
11. sixth day of the week

___ ___ a ___ ___ ___ ___ ___ ___ o ___ ___ o ___ .

Word Bank

bicycle	Friday	nearby	sign	tiny
die	lie	ripe	smile	wild
fight	life	shy	tight	wipe

G Dictation

Name _____

Listen and write the missing words and punctuation.

1. Tony _____ Stephen's _____

_____ _____ __

2. Mr. Valentino _____ Stephen

_____ _____ __

3. _____ _____ _____ shovel _____ _____

_____ _____ _____ __

H Proofreading

If a word is misspelled, fill in the oval by that word. If all the words are spelled correctly, fill in the oval by **no mistake**.

1. ⬭ busy
   ⬭ awake
   ⬭ bycycle
   ⬭ no mistake

4. ⬭ February
   ⬭ ly
   ⬭ shade
   ⬭ no mistake

7. ⬭ ripe
   ⬭ tite
   ⬭ shy
   ⬭ no mistake

2. ⬭ fite
   ⬭ carry
   ⬭ creek
   ⬭ no mistake

5. ⬭ field
   ⬭ heavy
   ⬭ nearbye
   ⬭ no mistake

8. ⬭ smile
   ⬭ mean
   ⬭ tinie
   ⬭ no mistake

3. ⬭ deep
   ⬭ Fryday
   ⬭ weigh
   ⬭ no mistake

6. ⬭ sighn
   ⬭ die
   ⬭ life
   ⬭ no mistake

9. ⬭ marry
   ⬭ wipe
   ⬭ wilde
   ⬭ no mistake

I | Game

Name _____

Help Mr. Valentino's class shovel the snow from Mrs. Swanson's driveway. Move one space for each word you or your team spells correctly from this week's word list.

Remember: God gets great glory when you do what is right!

J | Journaling

In your journal, make a list of kind things you could do to show respect for your elders.

A Preview

Write each word as your teacher says it.

Name _____

1. _____

2. _____

3. _____

4. _____

5. _____

6. _____

7. _____

8. _____

9. _____

10. _____

11. _____

12. _____

13. _____

14. _____

15. _____

Scripture

Colossians 3:13

Write each word in the correct word shape boxes. Next, in the word shape boxes, color the letter or letters that spell the sound of /ō/ in each word.

1. ago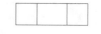

2. alone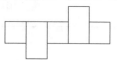

3. float

4. follow

5. goes

6. gold

7. open

8. owe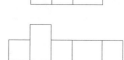

9. rode

10. rope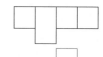

11. sew

12. shown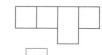

13. spoke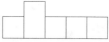

14. telephone

15. toast

C Hide and Seek

Name _____

Place an **X** on a coin for each word you spell correctly.

D Other Word Forms

Using the words below, follow the instructions given by your teacher.

floated	gone	openly	roping	speaking
floating	golden	openness	sewed	spoken
floats	loneliness	owed	sewing	telephoned
followed	lonely	owing	sewn	telephoning
follower	lonesome	ride	show	toasted
following	opened	rider	showed	toaster
go	opener	riding	showing	toasting
going	opening	roped	speak	

E Fun Ways to Spell

Initial the box of each activity you finish.

1.

Spell your words with chalk.

3.

Spell your words out of the letter box.

2.

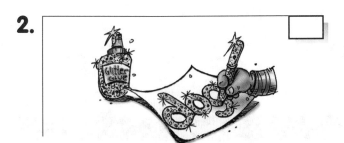

Spell your words with glitter glue.

4.

Spell your words on carpet.

127

      Name _____

Spelling Clues

Write the correct spelling words on the lines.

1. The little word **phone** is in the bigger word _____.

2. The little word **oat** is in the bigger word _____.

3. The little word **low** is in the bigger word _____.

4. The little word **go** is in the bigger words _____

and _____.

5. The little word **old** is in the bigger word _____.

6. The little word **pen** is in the bigger word _____.

7. The little word **we** is in the bigger word _____.

8. The little word **rod** is in the bigger word _____.

9. The little word **own** is in the bigger word _____.

10. The little word **poke** is in the bigger word _____.

11. The little word **one** is in the bigger word _____.

12. The little word **as** is in the bigger word _____.

13. Write the word in which /ō/ is spelled **ew**. _____

14. Write the word that rhymes with **soap**. _____

Dictionary Skills

Some dictionary entries have more than one meaning or definition. Read the entry word and its definitions. Write the number of the definition that matches the meaning of the bold word in each sentence.

rope   **1.** strong cord made from twisted fiber   **2.** to catch with a lasso

1. Father showed me how to **rope** a steer. _____

2. We watched a man making **rope** at the tractor show. _____

Word Bank

ago	follow	open	rope	spoke
alone	goes	owe	sew	telephone
float	gold	rode	shown	toast

G Dictation

Name _____

Listen and write the missing words and punctuation.

1. Kristin _____ _____ __ _____

_____ recipe__

2. _____ _____ _____ _____

____ ____ __

3. _____ ____ oven _____ _____

cookies ___ __ _____

H Proofreading

If a word is misspelled, fill in the oval by that word. If all the words are spelled correctly, fill in the oval by **no mistake**.

1. ◯ bicycle
   ◯ alone
   ◯ agoe
   ◯ no mistake

2. ◯ flote
   ◯ fight
   ◯ Friday
   ◯ no mistake

3. ◯ opin
   ◯ follow
   ◯ gold
   ◯ no mistake

4. ◯ owe
   ◯ goz
   ◯ nearby
   ◯ no mistake

5. ◯ lie
   ◯ sign
   ◯ roade
   ◯ no mistake

6. ◯ roap
   ◯ shown
   ◯ wipe
   ◯ no mistake

7. ◯ sew
   ◯ telefone
   ◯ tight
   ◯ no mistake

8. ◯ tiny
   ◯ wild
   ◯ toste
   ◯ no mistake

9. ◯ spoke
   ◯ twenty
   ◯ meal
   ◯ no mistake

I Game

Name _____

Complete the secret phrase by correctly spelling the words from this week's word list.

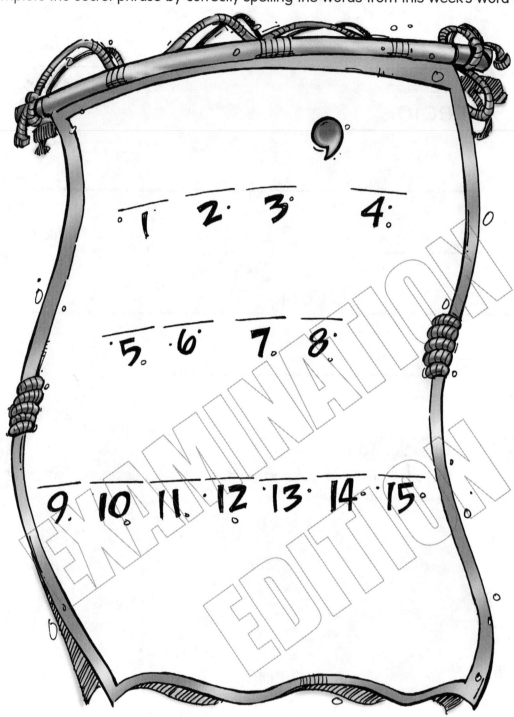

Remember: Forgive others the way Jesus has forgiven you!

J Journaling

In your journal, write a paragraph about a time when you forgave someone.

A Preview

Write each word as your teacher says it.

Name _____

1. _____

2. _____

3. _____

4. _____

5. _____

6. _____

7. _____

8. _____

9. _____

10. _____

11. _____

12. _____

13. _____

14. _____

15. _____

Scripture

Colossians 3:14

Name _____

Write each word in the correct word shape boxes. Next, in the word shape boxes, color the letter or letters that spell the sound of /ô/ in each word. Circle the words which have the silent consonants **gh**.

1. August

2. autumn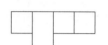

3. bought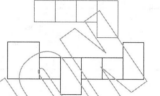

4. brought

5. cause

6. daughter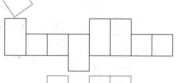

7. fought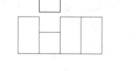

8. hall

9. paw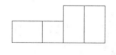

10. raw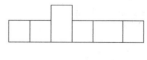

11. salt

12. song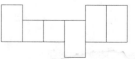

13. taught

14. upon

15. wall

C Hide and Seek

Place an **X** on a coin for each word you spell correctly.

D Other Word Forms

Using the words below, follow the instructions given by your teacher.

bring	daughters	rawest	teach
bringing	fight	salted	teaching
buy	fighting	saltier	walled
buying	halls	saltiest	walls
caused	pawing	salty	
causes	paws	singer	
causing	rawer	singing	

E Fun Ways to Spell

Initial the box of each activity you finish.

1.

Spell your words with pictures.

3.

Spell your words out loud.

2.

Spell your words with lemon juice.

4.

Spell your words with pipe cleaners.

Name _____

Word Sort

Write each spelling word under the correct heading.

au	**ou**	**a**
1. _____	6. _____	9. _____
2. _____	7. _____	10. _____
3. _____	8. _____	11. _____
4. _____		
5. _____	**aw**	**o**
	12. _____	14. _____
	13. _____	15. _____

ABC Order

Write the words from each group in alphabetical order.

daughter	cause	brought
1. _____	2. _____	3. _____
raw	wall	salt
4. _____	5. _____	6. _____
fought	bought	hall
7. _____	8. _____	9. _____
autumn	August	taught
10. _____	11. _____	12. _____

Word Bank

August	salt	taught	brought	hall
song	wall	bought	daughter	autumn
paw	upon	raw	fought	cause

Words with /ô/

G Dictation

Listen and write the missing words and punctuation.

1. _____ _____ _____ _____ _____

   _____ __ _____ _____ __

2. _____ _____ _____ _____ __ _____

   __ Chinese __

3. _____ swim _____ _____ _____

   __ __ _____ __

H Proofreading

If a word is misspelled, fill in the oval by that word. If all the words are spelled correctly, fill in the oval by **no mistake**.

1.
   ○ paw
   ○ ago
   ○ Awgust
   ○ no mistake

2.
   ○ autum
   ○ float
   ○ goes
   ○ no mistake

3.
   ○ open
   ○ bowght
   ○ rode
   ○ no mistake

4.
   ○ fought
   ○ salt
   ○ brouwt
   ○ no mistake

5.
   ○ cauze
   ○ song
   ○ rope
   ○ no mistake

6.
   ○ dawter
   ○ taught
   ○ telephone
   ○ no mistake

7.
   ○ upon
   ○ hal
   ○ toast
   ○ no mistake

8.
   ○ ripe
   ○ shy
   ○ woll
   ○ no mistake

9.
   ○ life
   ○ rauw
   ○ die
   ○ no mistake

I Game

Name _____

Glue on a piece of the puzzle-picture for each word you or your team spells correctly from this week's word list.

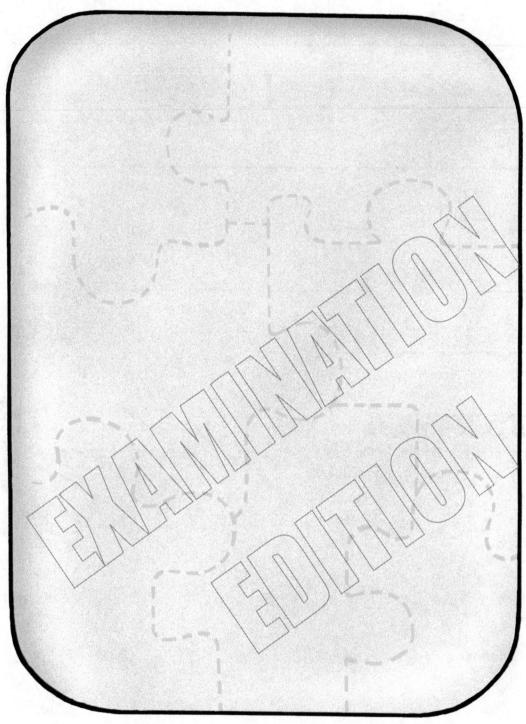

Remember: If you love God, do your best to get along with others.

J Journaling

In your journal, write about a time when you did not get along with someone. Finish by telling how you could have helped it not to happen.

A Preview

Write each word as your teacher says it.

Name _____

1. _____

2. _____

3. _____

4. _____

5. _____

6. _____

7. _____

8. _____

9. _____

10. _____

11. _____

12. _____

13. _____

14. _____

15. _____

Scripture

James 3:17

Name _____

Write each word in the correct word shape boxes. Next, in the word shape boxes, color the letters that spell the sound of **/ou/** in each word. Circle the words which begin with an **-r** or **-l** cluster.

1. allow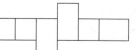

2. amount

3. anyhow

4. clown

5. crowd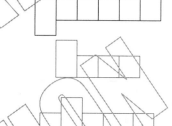

6. doubt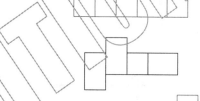

7. drown

8. ground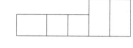

9. hour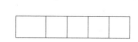

10. loud

11. mouse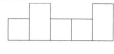

12. mouth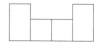

13. plow

14. power

15. shout

C Hide and Seek

Name _____

Place an **X** on a coin for each word you spell correctly.

D Other Word Forms

Using the words below, follow the instructions given by your teacher.

allowance	crowding	grounder	mouthful
allowed	crowds	groundless	powerful
allows	doubting	hourly	powerfully
amounted	doubtless	loudly	powerless
clowned	undoubtedly	loudness	shouted
clowning	drowned	mice	shouting
clowns	drowning	mouser	
crowded	grounded	mouthed	

E Fun Ways to Spell

Initial the box of each activity you finish.

1.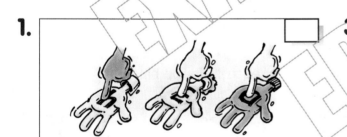

Spell your words in your classmate's hand.

3.

Spell your words using a tape recorder.

2.

Spell your words with paper cups.

4.

Spell your words with magazine clippings.

Name _____

Secret Code

Katelynn and Beth like to write notes in code to each other. Use their code to write your spelling words.

a	b	c	d	e	f	g	h	i	j	k	l	m	n	o	p	q	r	s	t	u	v	w	x	y	z
1	2	3	4	5	6	7	8	9	10	11	12	13	14	15	16	17	18	19	20	21	22	23	24	25	26

1. _ _ _ _ _
   1 12 12 15 23

2. _ _ _ _ _
   19 8 15 21 20

3. _ _ _ _ _
   3 12 15 23 14

4. _ _ _ _ _
   13 15 21 19 5

5. _ _ _ _ _
   16 15 23 5 18

6. _ _ _ _ _ _
   1 13 15 21 14 20

7. _ _ _ _ _
   4 15 21 2 20

8. _ _ _ _
   8 15 21 18

9. _ _ _ _ _
   13 15 21 20 8

10. _ _ _ _ _ _
    7 18 15 21 14 4

11. _ _ _ _
    12 15 21 4

12. _ _ _ _ _ _
    1 14 25 8 15 23

13. _ _ _ _ _
    3 18 15 23 4

14. _ _ _ _
    16 12 15 23

15. _ _ _ _ _
    4 18 15 23 14

Dictionary Skills

Write the spelling word that would be the entry word for each definition below.

1. _____ to say something by only moving your lips

2. _____ to let someone do something

3. _____ how much there is of something

4. _____ the surface of the earth

5. _____ forms of energy such as electricity

Word Bank

allow	clown	drown	loud	plow
amount	crowd	ground	mouse	power
anyhow	doubt	hour	mouth	shout

G Dictation

Name _____

Listen and write the missing words and punctuation.

1. ___ _____ ___ ___ ___ ___ ___

___ ___ ___ ___ ___

2. ___ _____, Laney, ___ ___

___ ___ ___ ___ ___ ___

3. ___ ___ ___ _____

_____ ___ watch _____ ___

H Proofreading

If a word is misspelled, fill in the oval by that word. If all the words are spelled correctly, fill in the oval by **no mistake**.

1. ⭕ alow
   ⭕ pour
   ⭕ August
   ⭕ no mistake

2. ⭕ autumn
   ⭕ amownt
   ⭕ hour
   ⭕ no mistake

3. ⭕ ground
   ⭕ bought
   ⭕ inyhow
   ⭕ no mistake

4. ⭕ croud
   ⭕ mouth
   ⭕ brought
   ⭕ no mistake

5. ⭕ plow
   ⭕ dout
   ⭕ cause
   ⭕ no mistake

6. ⭕ droun
   ⭕ shout
   ⭕ daughter
   ⭕ no mistake

7. ⭕ hall
   ⭕ lowd
   ⭕ raw
   ⭕ no mistake

8. ⭕ wall
   ⭕ owe
   ⭕ mowse
   ⭕ no mistake

9. ⭕ powir
   ⭕ shown
   ⭕ song
   ⭕ no mistake

I Game

Beth realizes she is not treating the new girl in school, Laney, the way Jesus says she should. Go with Beth as she invites Laney to her birthday slumber party. Move one space for each word you or your team spells correctly from this week's word list.

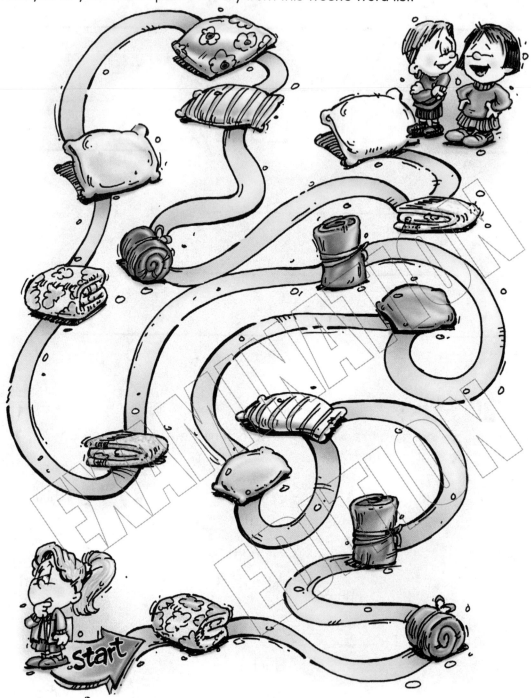

start

Remember: Plant yourself firmly in God's love. He will never fail you!

J Journaling

In your journal, make a list of at least five ways you could make a new member of your class feel welcome. Title your list.

A Preview

Write each word as your teacher says it.

Name _____

1. _____

2. _____

3. _____

4. _____

5. _____

6. _____

7. _____

8. _____

9. _____

10. _____

11. _____

12. _____

13. _____

14. _____

15. _____

Scripture

Ephesians 4:2

Name _____

Write each word in the correct word shape boxes. Next, in the word shape boxes, color the letters that spell the sound of /ôr/ in each word. Circle the words in which /ôr/ is spelled **our**.

1. airport

2. corner

3. course

4. floor

5. fort

6. fourth

7. horn

8. order

9. pour

10. report

11. score

12. sore

13. sport

14. storm

15. wore

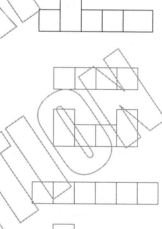
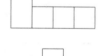
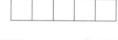
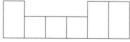

C Hide and Seek

Place an **X** on a coin for each word you spell correctly.

D Other Word Forms

Using the words below, follow the instructions given by your teacher.

airports	four	scored	storming
cornered	horns	scores	stormy
corners	ordered	scoring	wear
coursed	ordering	sorely	wearing
coursing	orders	soreness	wears
floors	poured	sports	
flooring	pouring	sporty	
forts	pours	stormed	

E Fun Ways to Spell

Initial the box of each activity you finish.

1.

Spell your words with markers.

3.

Spell your words while snapping.

2.

Spell your words with letter tiles.

4.

Spell your words with paint.

F Working with Words

Name ______________________

Complete the Word

Fill in the missing letters to complete each word.

1. _ o r _ _ _
2. _ o r _
3. _ _ _ o r _
4. _ o r _
5. _ _ _ _ o r _
6. _ _ _ o r
7. _ o r _
8. _ _ o r _
9. o r _ _ _
10. _ _ o r _
11. _ o r _
12. _ _ o r _
13. _ o u r _ _
14. _ o u r
15. _ o u r _ _

1. place where two streets come together
2. an army post
3. writing down the facts
4. hard bone on an animal's head
5. place to land airplanes
6. surface of room we walk on
7. painful
8. game played for fun
9. tell someone what to do
10. a record of points
11. had on clothes
12. wild weather
13. path to race on
14. to rain hard
15. comes before fifth

Word Bank

airport	floor	horn	report	sport
corner	fort	order	score	storm
course	fourth	pour	sore	wore

G Dictation

Name _____

Listen and write the missing words and punctuation.

1. Christopher _____ ___ _____

_____ _____ _____ _____ _

2. _____ _____ _____ Daniel ___ _____

_____ _____ _

3. _____ _____ _____ _____ carnival _____

___ _____, _____ _____

H Proofreading

If a word is misspelled, fill in the oval by that word. If all the words are spelled correctly, fill in the oval by **no mistake**.

1. ◯ allow
   ◯ areport
   ◯ amount
   ◯ no mistake

2. ◯ corse
   ◯ wore
   ◯ anyhow
   ◯ no mistake

3. ◯ fort
   ◯ clown
   ◯ flore
   ◯ no mistake

4. ◯ fuorth
   ◯ crowd
   ◯ horn
   ◯ no mistake

5. ◯ doubt
   ◯ order
   ◯ scor
   ◯ no mistake

6. ◯ drown
   ◯ cornir
   ◯ loud
   ◯ no mistake

7. ◯ storn
   ◯ mouse
   ◯ power
   ◯ no mistake

8. ◯ sport
   ◯ repoort
   ◯ clown
   ◯ no mistake

9. ◯ soare
   ◯ pour
   ◯ mouth
   ◯ no mistake

I Game

Name _____

Work patiently with Daniel to decorate for the school carnival. Move one space for each word you or your team spells correctly from this week's word list.

Remember: We can get all the patience we need from Jesus.

J Journaling

In your journal, write a pledge (like a promise) that you will try to be patient with your family, your friends, your classmates, and others.

Write each spelling word on the line as your teacher says it.

1. _____   7. _____

2. _____   8. _____

3. _____   9. _____

4. _____   10. _____

5. _____   11. _____

6. _____   12. _____

B **Test-Sentences**

Write the sentences on the lines below, correcting each misspelled word, as well as all capitalization and punctuation errors. There are two misspelled words in each sentence.

The tiney petals will flote on the water.

1. _____

our teacher tawt us a silly saung.

2. _____

There was a funny cloun at the cornir

3. _____

C Test-Dictation

Name _____

Listen and write the missing words and punctuation.

1. ___ ___ ___ ___ ___ ___ ___ ___

2. ___ ___ ___ ___ ___ ___ ___ ___

3. ___ ___ ___ ___ ___

4. _____ near ___ __

___ __ ___ ___ ___ ___

eight dollars __

D Test-Proofreading

If a word is misspelled, fill in the oval by that word. If all the words are spelled correctly, fill in the oval by **no mistake**.

1. ◯ die
   ◯ score
   ◯ upon
   ◯ no mistake

2. ◯ shye
   ◯ taught
   ◯ crowd
   ◯ no mistake

3. ◯ loud
   ◯ shown
   ◯ sighn
   ◯ no mistake

4. ◯ gold
   ◯ ground
   ◯ wore
   ◯ no mistake

5. ◯ mouse
   ◯ roap
   ◯ float
   ◯ no mistake

6. ◯ spoek
   ◯ August
   ◯ horn
   ◯ no mistake

7. ◯ bought
   ◯ autum
   ◯ fourth
   ◯ no mistake

8. ◯ fought
   ◯ report
   ◯ order
   ◯ no mistake

9. ◯ sew
   ◯ powir
   ◯ anyhow
   ◯ no mistake

Name _____

If a word is misspelled, color the nut by that word.

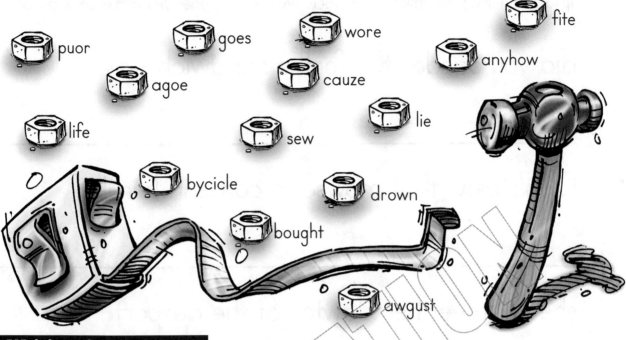

F Writing Assessment

Write about a time when you worked with "members of God's household" to help someone, or write about a time when "members of God's household" worked together to help you.

_____

_____

_____

_____

_____

_____

_____

_____

Scripture

Ephesians 2:19

G Test-Sentences

Name _____

Write the sentences on the lines below, correcting each misspelled word, as well as all capitalization and punctuation errors. There are two misspelled words in each sentence.

did you oarder the forthe sandwich

1. _____

Don't alow that mowse to come in here!

2. _____

she will meet her dawter at the aerport.

3. _____

H Test-Words

Write each spelling word on the line as your teacher says it.

1. _____   7. _____

2. _____   8. _____

3. _____   9. _____

4. _____   10. _____

5. _____   11. _____

6. _____   12. _____

Name _____

If a word is spelled correctly, fill in the oval under **Correct**. If the word is misspelled, fill in the oval under **Incorrect**, and spell the word correctly on the blank.

		Correct	Incorrect	
1.	horn	○	○	_____
2.	report	○	○	_____
3.	skor	○	○	_____
4.	sor	○	○	_____
5.	sport	○	○	_____
6.	storm	○	○	_____
7.	mowth	○	○	_____
8.	plow	○	○	_____
9.	showt	○	○	_____
10.	paw	○	○	_____
11.	raw	○	○	_____
12.	upon	○	○	_____

Score points for each review word or Other Word Form you or your team spells correctly.

Remember: When you know Jesus, you are a part of His family.

Spelling Is Fun!

ABC's

This certificate is awarded to

_____

for practicing the following words, by doing terrific spelling activities, and playing great spelling games!

Date _____

bicycle	ago	August	allow	airport
die	alone	autumn	amount	corner
fight	float	bought	anyhow	course
Friday	follow	brought	clown	floor
lie	goes	cause	crowd	fort
life	gold	daughter	doubt	fourth
nearby	open	fought	drown	horn
ripe	owe	hall	ground	order
shy	rode	paw	hour	pour
sign	rope	raw	loud	report
smile	sew	salt	mouse	score
tight	shown	song	mouth	sore
tiny	spoke	taught	plow	sport
wild	telephone	upon	power	storm
wipe	toast	wall	shout	wore

Dear Parent,

　　We are about to begin a new spelling unit containing five weekly lessons. A set of fifteen words will be studied each week. All the words will be reviewed in the sixth week. Values based on the Scriptures listed below will be taught in each lesson.

Lesson 25	Lesson 26	Lesson 27	Lesson 28	Lesson 29
alarm	center	able	burn	brook
apart	December	April	dirt	bushes
argue	dollar	bottle	early	cookie
army	driver	candle	earn	football
artist	forget	cattle	herd	good-bye
bark	hammer	eagle	hurry	hood
charge	later	handle	learn	hook
March	mirror	metal	person	neighborhood
mark	November	middle	return	notebook
market	remember	needle	Saturday	pulley
park	river	saddle	search	push
shark	silver	sprinkle	September	shook
sharp	sugar	squirrel	serve	wolf
smart	summer	travel	thirty	woman
start	wonder	turtle	worse	wool

| Eph. 3:17-19 | 2 Thess. 3:5 | James 4:11 | Romans 15:5 | 1 Timothy 2:1 |

A Preview

Name _____

Write each word as your teacher says it.

1. _____

2. _____

3. _____

4. _____

5. _____

6. _____

7. _____

8. _____

9. _____

10. _____

11. _____

12. _____

13. _____

14. _____

15. _____

Scripture

Ephesians 3:17–19

B Word Shapes

Name _____

Write each word in the correct word shape boxes. Next, in the word shape boxes, color the letters that spell the sound of **/är/** in each word. Circle the words that have the digraph **/ch/** or **/sh/**.

1. alarm

2. apart

3. argue

4. army

5. artist

6. bark

7. charge

8. March

9. mark

10. market

11. park

12. shark

13. sharp

14. smart

15. start

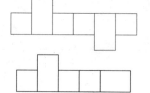

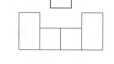

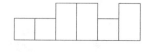

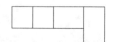

C Hide and Seek

Place an **X** on a coin for each word you spell correctly.

D Other Word Forms

Using the words below, follow the instructions given by your teacher.

alarmed	artists	discharge	marketplace	sharpness
alarming	barked	marked	parking	smarted
alarms	barking	marker	parks	smartly
arguing	barks	marking	sharks	smartness
argument	embarked	remarkable	sharpen	started
armies	charged	marketable	sharpener	starting
artistic	charging	marketing	sharply	starts

E Fun Ways to Spell

Initial the box of each activity you finish.

1. ☐

Spell your words with puzzles.

3. ☐

Spell your words in rhythm.

2. ☐

Spell your words with sidewalk chalk.

4. ☐

Spell your words with play dough.

159

F Working with Words

Name _____

Spelling Clues

Write the correct spelling words on the lines.

1. The little word **arm** is in the bigger words _____ and _____.

2. The little word **art** is in the bigger words _____, _____, _____, and _____.

3. The little word **ark** is in the bigger words _____, _____, _____, _____, and _____.

4. The little word **harp** is in the bigger word _____.

5. The little word **arch** is in the bigger word _____.

6. Write the words which have the digraph /ch/. _____ _____

7. Write the words which have the digraph /sh/. _____ _____

8. Write the word in which /ū/ is spelled **ue**. _____

Dictionary Skills

Use the following information to tell about the dictionary parts below.

barge   base

bark the hard covering on the outside of a tree: Birch bark is used for canoes.

1. entry word _____

2. definition _____

3. guide words _____ _____

4. sample sentence _____

Word Bank

alarm	army	charge	market	sharp
apart	artist	March	park	smart
argue	bark	mark	shark	start

160

G Dictation

Name _____

Listen and write the missing words and punctuation.

1. ____ ____ ____ ___ thunder

____ Rosa ____ __ ____ _

2. ____ ____ ____ ___ stack ___

____ __ ____ ____ ___ _

3. Carlos ___ Rosa ____ ____

__ ____ _

H Proofreading

If a word is misspelled, fill in the oval by that word. If all the words are spelled correctly, fill in the oval by **no mistake**.

1. ◯ alarm
   ◯ apatr
   ◯ airport
   ◯ no mistake

2. ◯ army
   ◯ course
   ◯ floor
   ◯ no mistake

3. ◯ bark
   ◯ corner
   ◯ artest
   ◯ no mistake

4. ◯ argu
   ◯ bark
   ◯ fourth
   ◯ no mistake

5. ◯ report
   ◯ charg
   ◯ shark
   ◯ no mistake

6. ◯ sharp
   ◯ Martch
   ◯ score
   ◯ no mistake

7. ◯ sore
   ◯ start
   ◯ marck
   ◯ no mistake

8. ◯ markit
   ◯ storm
   ◯ fort
   ◯ no mistake

9. ◯ life
   ◯ snart
   ◯ loud
   ◯ no mistake

I | Game

Name _____

Help Rosa, Maria, and Carlos stack wood for Grandpa Joe and Grandma Ruth. Move one space for each word you or your team spells correctly from this week's word list.

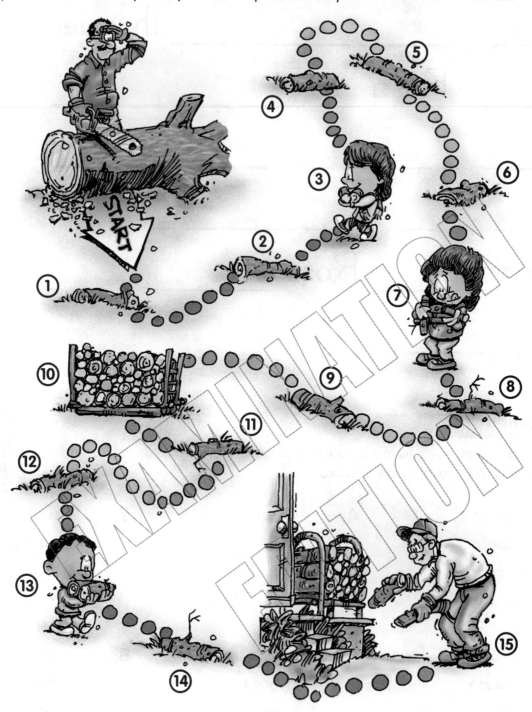

Remember: God's love for us is ENORMOUS!

J | Journaling

In your journal, write about what kind of tree you're like now and what kind of tree you want to be like.

A Preview

Write each word as your teacher says it.

Name _____

1. _____

2. _____

3. _____

4. _____

5. _____

6. _____

7. _____

8. _____   12. _____

9. _____   13. _____

10. _____   14. _____

11. _____   15. _____

Scripture

2 Thessalonians 3:5

Write each word in the correct word shape boxes. Next, in the word shape boxes, color the letters that spell the sound of **/ər/** in each word.

1. center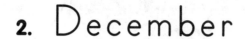

2. December

3. dollar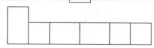

4. driver

5. forget

6. hammer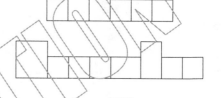

7. later

8. mirror

9. November

10. remember

11. river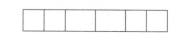

12. silver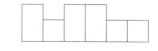

13. sugar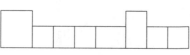

14. summer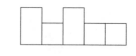

15. wonder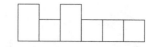

164

C Hide and Seek

Place an **X** on a coin for each word you spell correctly.

D Other Word Forms

Using the words below, follow the instructions given by your teacher.

centered	drove	lately	remembered	sugaring
centering	forgetful	lateness	remembering	sugary
centers	forgetfulness	later	remembers	summery
dollars	hammered	latest	silvered	wondered
drive	hammering	mirrored	silvering	wonderful
driven	hammers	mirroring	silvery	wondering
driving	late	mirrors	sugared	wonders

E Fun Ways to Spell

Initial the box of each activity you finish.

1.

Spell your words with chalk.

3.

Spell your words out of the letter box.

2.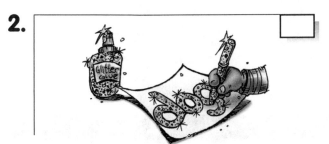

Spell your words with glitter glue.

4.

Spell your words on carpet.

165

Syllables

These are examples of entry words. Count how many syllables each word has and write the number on the line.

1. a•larm _____   **3.** grand•fa•ther _____

2. shout _____

Find each of the words below in the dictionary. Write them in syllables, putting a dot between the syllables.

1. center _____   **9.** December _____

2. dollar _____   **10.** driver _____

3. hammer _____   **11.** forget _____

4. later _____   **12.** mirror _____

5. November _____   **13.** remember _____

6. river _____   **14.** silver _____

7. sugar _____   **15.** summer _____

8. wonder _____

Word Sort

Write each spelling word under the correct heading for the /ər/ spelling.

-er	-er	-ar
1. _____	**7.** _____	**12.** _____
2. _____	**8.** _____	**13.** _____
3. _____	**9.** _____	
4. _____	**10.** _____	-or
5. _____	**11.** _____	**14.** _____
6. _____		**15.** _____

Word Bank

center	driver	later	remember	sugar
December	forget	mirror	river	summer
dollar	hammer	November	silver	wonder

26

G Dictation

Name _____

Listen and write the missing words and punctuation.

1. _____ _____ Christopher _____ _____

   __ __ _____ __ _____ _____ __

2. _____ _____ _____ _____ spoon ___

   ___ _____ bowl __

3. _____ _____ _____ cereal ___ __ ___

   ___ _____ ___ _____ _____ __

H Proofreading

If a word is misspelled, fill in the oval by that word. If all the words are spelled correctly, fill in the oval by **no mistake**.

1. ◯ driver
   ◯ apart
   ◯ cinter
   ◯ no mistake

2. ◯ Desember
   ◯ artist
   ◯ argue
   ◯ no mistake

3. ◯ charge
   ◯ dollor
   ◯ March
   ◯ no mistake

4. ◯ smart
   ◯ mark
   ◯ hamer
   ◯ no mistake

5. ◯ ferget
   ◯ market
   ◯ remember
   ◯ no mistake

6. ◯ river
   ◯ shark
   ◯ laeter
   ◯ no mistake

7. ◯ summer
   ◯ merer
   ◯ silver
   ◯ no mistake

8. ◯ alarm
   ◯ november
   ◯ start
   ◯ no mistake

9. ◯ horn
   ◯ wonder
   ◯ sugar
   ◯ no mistake

I | Game

Name _____

Glue on a piece of the puzzle-picture for each word you or your team spells correctly from this week's word list.

Remember: God can help you to learn patience.

J | Journaling

In your journal, write a letter to your parents. Tell them what you really like about them and how much you love them.

A Preview

Write each word as your teacher says it.

Name _____

1. _____

2. _____

3. _____

4. _____

5. _____

6. _____

7. _____

8. _____

9. _____

10. _____

11. _____

12. _____

13. _____

14. _____

15. _____

Scripture

James 4:11

Name _____

Write each word in the correct word shape boxes. Next, in the word shape boxes, color the letters that spell the sound of /əl/ in each word.

1. able

2. April

3. bottle

4. candle

5. cattle

6. eagle

7. handle

8. metal

9. middle

10. needle

11. saddle

12. sprinkle

13. squirrel

14. travel

15. turtle

C Hide and Seek

Name _____

Place an **X** on a coin for each word you spell correctly.

D Other Word Forms

Using the words below, follow the instructions given by your teacher.

bottled	handled	saddled	traveling
bottling	handles	saddles	travels
candles	handling	saddling	turtleneck
cattleman	metallic	sprinkled	turtles
disable	needled	sprinkles	
enable	needles	sprinkling	
eaglet	needling	traveled	

E Fun Ways to Spell

Initial the box of each activity you finish.

1.

Spell your words with pictures.

3.

Spell your words out loud.

2.

Spell your words with lemon juice.

4.

Spell your words with pipe cleaners.

Sentence Fun

Write the correct spelling word on the line to complete each sentence.

1. The _____ gave very little light.

2. We should be _____ to come over.

3. We need to round up the _____ before dark.

4. The _____ circled over the lake.

5. A _____ does not walk very fast.

6. The _____ in the compass points north.

7. It rained every afternoon in _____.

8. The furry _____ was not afraid of us.

9. At camp, I learned how to _____ a horse.

10. It is fun to _____ to new places.

11. As we set up our tent, it began to _____.

12. Rosa raised her hand during the _____ of class.

13. He spilled the _____ of water on his homework.

14. The _____ chest we dug up was very heavy.

15. The sign said not to _____ the glass dishes.

Word Sort

Write the spelling words under the correct heading.

-el	-al	-il
1. _____	3. _____	4. _____
2. _____		

Word Bank

able	candle	handle	needle	squirrel
April	cattle	metal	saddle	travel
bottle	eagle	middle	sprinkle	turtle

G Dictation

Name _____

Listen and write the missing words and punctuation.

1. _____ _____ flew _____ ____ ___

_____ _____ ___ _____ _____ branch _

2. _____ _____ _____ _____ _____ ___

____ Rosa _____ _

3. _____ _____ ___ _____ _____

_____ ____ _____ _

H Proofreading

If a word is misspelled, fill in the oval by that word. If all the words are spelled correctly, fill in the oval by **no mistake**.

1. ◯ cattle
   ◯ center
   ◯ abel
   ◯ no mistake

2. ◯ Aprul
   ◯ December
   ◯ November
   ◯ no mistake

3. ◯ botel
   ◯ hammer
   ◯ forget
   ◯ no mistake

4. ◯ candel
   ◯ middle
   ◯ later
   ◯ no mistake

5. ◯ needle
   ◯ mirror
   ◯ eegle
   ◯ no mistake

6. ◯ saddle
   ◯ metel
   ◯ sharp
   ◯ no mistake

7. ◯ park
   ◯ turtle
   ◯ sprinckle
   ◯ no mistake

8. ◯ squirrle
   ◯ driver
   ◯ bark
   ◯ no mistake

9. ◯ river
   ◯ travele
   ◯ summer
   ◯ no mistake

I Game

Name _____

Complete the secret phrase by correctly spelling the words from this week's word list.

Remember: We are disobeying God when we say mean things about others.

J Journaling

Look at your classmates sitting on either side, in front of, and behind you. In your journal, write one or two compliments about each of these classmates. Share your compliments with them.

A Preview

Write each word as your teacher says it.

Name _____

1. _____

2. _____

3. _____

4. _____

5. _____

6. _____

7. _____

8. _____

9. _____

10. _____

11. _____

12. _____

13. _____

14. _____

15. _____

Scripture

Romans 15:5

Name _____

Write each word in the correct word shape boxes. Next, in the word shape boxes, color the letters that spell the sound of **/ûr/** or **/ər/** in each word.

1. burn

2. dirt

3. early

4. earn

5. herd

6. hurry

7. learn

8. person

9. return

10. Saturday

11. search

12. September

13. serve

14. thirty

15. worse

C Hide and Seek

Place an **X** on a coin for each word you spell correctly.

D Other Word Forms

Using the words below, follow the instructions given by your teacher.

burned	earliest	hurries	returnable	servant
burning	earned	hurrying	returned	served
burnt	earning	learned	returning	serviceable
dirtier	earnings	learning	returns	serving
dirtiest	herded	learns	searched	worsen
dirty	herding	personable	searcher	worst
dirtying	herds	personal	searches	
earlier	hurried	personalize	searching	

E Fun Ways to Spell

Initial the box of each activity you finish.

1.

Spell your words in your classmate's hand.

2.

Spell your words with paper cups.

3.

Spell your words using a tape recorder.

4.

Spell your words with magazine clippings.

Riddles in Rhyme

Write the spelling word that completes each rhyme.

1. I am sure that he is hurt.

He fell face down into the _____.

2. I dropped my offering in the church,

So my mother helped me _____.

3. We cut each sandwich in a curve,

And placed them on a plate to _____.

4. Matches! Candles! Can't she learn,

To keep away from things that _____!

5. One day I always can remember,

My birthday is the third of _____.

6. Matthew, with the hair so curly,

Always gets to school quite _____.

7. To buy that game, my big concern,

Is how much money I need to _____.

8. Around the tree the squirrels scurry.

They must be in an awful _____.

9. I think we'd better call the nurse.

Before the patient gets much _____.

10. The cowboy could not hear a word,

Surrounded by the noisy _____.

Word Bank

burn	earn	learn	Saturday	serve
dirt	herd	person	search	thirty
early	hurry	return	September	worse

G Dictation

Listen and write the missing words and punctuation.

1. Tony ____ ____ ____ ____ ____ ____

____ ____ ____ ____ ____ ____

2. ____ ____ ____ ____ ____ inside ____

____ important ____ ____ ____ ____

3. Tony ____ ____ ____ ____ ____

____ ____ ____ ____ ____ ____

H Proofreading

If a word is misspelled, fill in the oval by that word. If all the words are spelled correctly, fill in the oval by **no mistake**.

1. ◯ return
   ◯ bern
   ◯ able
   ◯ no mistake

2. ◯ dert
   ◯ April
   ◯ bottle
   ◯ no mistake

3. ◯ candle
   ◯ erly
   ◯ eagle
   ◯ no mistake

4. ◯ earn
   ◯ search
   ◯ metal
   ◯ no mistake

5. ◯ hird
   ◯ sprinkle
   ◯ travel
   ◯ no mistake

6. ◯ hury
   ◯ squirrel
   ◯ September
   ◯ no mistake

7. ◯ lern
   ◯ serve
   ◯ cattle
   ◯ no mistake

8. ◯ thirty
   ◯ persen
   ◯ wonder
   ◯ no mistake

9. ◯ silver
   ◯ worse
   ◯ saterday
   ◯ no mistake

I Game

Name _____

Tony learned to be proud of his cousin and treat her with kindness. Follow Tony to listen to Heather play the piano by moving one space for each word you or your team spells correctly from this week's word list.

Remember: Ask Jesus to put His attitude of love for others in your heart.

J Journaling

In your journal, write a paragraph about how you should treat people who are not beautiful on the outside.

A Preview

Write each word as your teacher says it.

Name _____

1. _____

2. _____

3. _____

4. _____

5. _____

6. _____

7. _____

8. _____ 12. _____

9. _____ 13. _____

10. _____ 14. _____

11. _____ 15. _____

Scripture

I Timothy 2:1

Write each word in the correct word shape boxes. Next, in the word shape boxes, color the letter or letters that spell the sound of /ù/ in each word. Circle the four compound words.

1. brook

2. bushes

3. cookie

4. football

5. good–bye

6. hood

7. hook

8. neighborhood

9. notebook

10. pulley

11. push

12. shook

13. wolf

14. woman

15. wool

C Hide and Seek

Place an **X** on a coin for each word you spell correctly.

D Other Word Forms

Using the words below, follow the instructions given by your teacher.

brooklet	neighborhoods	shake	woolen
bush	hooks	shakes	woollier
bushy	notebooks	shaking	woolliest
cookies	pulleys	wolfish	woolly
footballs	pushed	wolves	
good–byes	pushes	womanly	
hooded	pushing	women	

E Fun Ways to Spell

Initial the box of each activity you finish.

1.

Spell your words with markers.

3.

Spell your words while snapping.

2.

Spell your words with letter tiles.

4.

Spell your words with paint.

Missing Letters

Fill in the missing letter or letters that spell the sound of /u̇/.

1. h ___ ___ k   **6.** br ___ ___ k   **11.** w ___ ___ l

2. w ___ man   **7.** p ___ sh   **12.** neighborh ___ ___ d

3. b ___ shes   **8.** w ___ lf   **13.** g ___ ___ d–bye

4. sh ___ ___ k   **9.** p ___ lley   **14.** f ___ ___ tball

5. c ___ ___ kie   **10.** h ___ ___ d   **15.** noteb ___ ___ k

Clues

Write the spelling word that matches each clue.

1. fastener or _____   **8.** winch or _____

2. shove or _____   **9.** community or _____

3. sweet treat or _____   **10.** stream or _____

4. shivered or _____   **11.** sheep fur or _____

5. shrubs or _____   **12.** lady or _____

6. head gear or _____   **13.** ball game or _____

7. farewell or _____   **14.** binder or _____

Dictionary Skills

Some dictionary entries have more than one meaning or definition. Read the entry word and its definitions. Write the number of the definition that matches the meaning of the bold word in each sentence.

wolf   **1.** wild mammal related to a dog that hunts in a pack   **2.** to eat quickly and greedily

1. The hungry man began to **wolf** down his dinner. _____

2. The **wolf** chased a rabbit. _____

Word Bank

brook	football	hook	pulley	wolf
bushes	good-bye	neighborhood	push	woman
cookie	hood	notebook	shook	wool

G Dictation

Name _____

Listen and write the missing words and punctuation.

1. _____ _____ _____ _____ _____ aside

_____ _____ _____ _____ _____ _____ _

2. _____ drove ___ Sarah's _____

_____ _____ _____ _____ _____ _____ _

3. Sarah _____ _____ _____ _____

waved _____ Mrs. Bentley_

H Proofreading

If a word is misspelled, fill in the oval by that word. If all the words are spelled correctly, fill in the oval by **no mistake**.

1. ⬭ hood
   ⬭ brooke
   ⬭ burn
   ⬭ no mistake

2. ⬭ booshes
   ⬭ hook
   ⬭ dirt
   ⬭ no mistake

3. ⬭ herd
   ⬭ hurry
   ⬭ cooky
   ⬭ no mistake

4. ⬭ football
   ⬭ push
   ⬭ learn
   ⬭ no mistake

5. ⬭ shook
   ⬭ person
   ⬭ goodby
   ⬭ no mistake

6. ⬭ neborhood
   ⬭ early
   ⬭ woman
   ⬭ no mistake

7. ⬭ notbook
   ⬭ wool
   ⬭ Saturday
   ⬭ no mistake

8. ⬭ serve
   ⬭ puley
   ⬭ turtle
   ⬭ no mistake

9. ⬭ middle
   ⬭ wofl
   ⬭ search
   ⬭ no mistake

I | Game

Name _____

Join Mr. Valentino's class as they pray for God's mercy on the special people on their list.
Move one space for each word you or your team spells correctly from this week's word list.

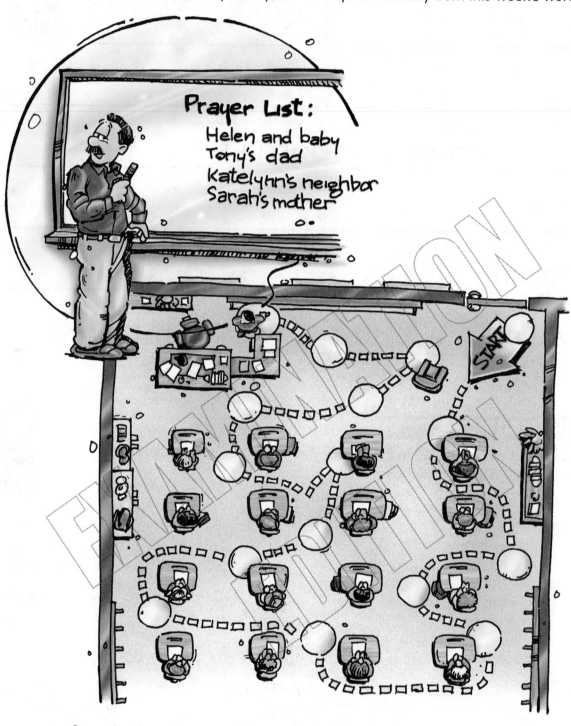

Remember: Spend a lot of time in prayer for other people!

J | Journaling

In your journal, start a prayer list . Write the name of each person you
are going to pray for and what he or she needs. You may add to your
prayer list any time.

Write each spelling word on the line as your teacher says it.

1. _____

2. _____

3. _____

4. _____

5. _____

6. _____

7. _____

8. _____

9. _____

10. _____

11. _____

12. _____

B Test-Sentences

Write the sentences on the lines below, correcting each misspelled word, as well as all capitalization and punctuation errors. There are two misspelled words in each sentence.

this sharck has hundreds of shapr teeth

1. _____

There are therty days in septimber

2. _____

a small tertel sat by the quiet brooke,

3. _____

C Test-Dictation

Name _____

Listen and write the missing words and punctuation.

1. _____ _____ _____ _____ _____ __

2. _____ _____ _____ _____ board __

3. _____ _____ _____ _____ _____

looks _____ _____ _____ bill __

4. _____ _____ _____ empty _____ _____

_____ _____ _____

D Test-Proofreading

If a word is misspelled, fill in the oval by that word. If all the words are spelled correctly, fill in the oval by **no mistake**.

1. ◯ Decimber
   ◯ dollar
   ◯ sugar
   ◯ no mistake

2. ◯ market
   ◯ remember
   ◯ handel
   ◯ no mistake

3. ◯ March
   ◯ center
   ◯ wonder
   ◯ no mistake

4. ◯ wolf
   ◯ later
   ◯ dirt
   ◯ no mistake

5. ◯ sharp
   ◯ allarm
   ◯ able
   ◯ no mistake

6. ◯ botel
   ◯ park
   ◯ brook
   ◯ no mistake

7. ◯ summer
   ◯ silvir
   ◯ worse
   ◯ no mistake

8. ◯ squirrel
   ◯ football
   ◯ good-bye
   ◯ no mistake

9. ◯ river
   ◯ argue
   ◯ mettal
   ◯ no mistake

E Test-Shapes

If a word is misspelled, color the candy by that word.

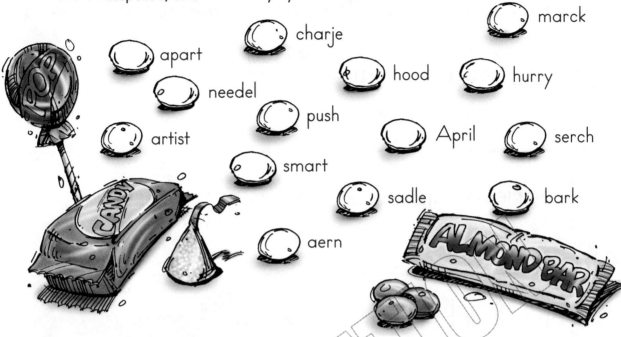

apart
charje
marck
needel
hood
hurry
artist
push
April
serch
smart
sadle
bark
aern

F Writing Assessment

Make a menu of three balanced meals you could eat in one day.

_____ _____ _____
_____ _____ _____
_____ _____ _____
_____ _____ _____
_____ _____ _____
_____ _____ _____
_____ _____ _____
_____ _____ _____

Scripture

James 1:5

Review

Lesson

30

G Test-Sentences

Name _____

Write the sentences on the lines below, correcting each misspelled word, as well as all capitalization and punctuation errors. There are two misspelled words in each sentence.

does a wofl have fur or woul

1. _____

the drievr can parck the bus over there

2. _____

You will not find an eegel in the booshez?

3. _____

H Test-Words

Write each spelling word on the line as your teacher says it.

1. _____   7. _____

2. _____   8. _____

3. _____   9. _____

4. _____   10. _____

5. _____   11. _____

6. _____   12. _____

Name _____

If a word is spelled correctly, fill in the oval under **Correct**. If the word is misspelled, fill in the oval under **Incorrect**, and spell the word correctly on the blank.

	Correct	Incorrect	
1. hammer	○	○	_____
2. argew	○	○	_____
3. november	○	○	_____
4. squirle	○	○	_____
5. candel	○	○	_____
6. army	○	○	_____
7. purson	○	○	_____
8. neyberhood	○	○	_____
9. hook	○	○	_____
10. pully	○	○	_____
11. werse	○	○	_____
12. herd	○	○	_____

Score points for each review word or Other Word Form you or your team spells correctly.

Review

Lesson

30

Remember: God has answers to your questions. Ask Him!

Spelling Is Fun!

This certificate is awarded to

_____

for practicing the following words, by doing terrific spelling activities, and playing great spelling games!

Date _____

alarm	center	able	burn	brook
apart	December	April	dirt	bushes
argue	dollar	bottle	early	cookie
army	driver	candle	earn	football
artist	forget	cattle	herd	good-bye
bark	hammer	eagle	hurry	hood
charge	later	handle	learn	hook
March	mirror	metal	person	neighborhood
mark	November	middle	return	notebook
market	remember	needle	Saturday	pulley
park	river	saddle	search	push
shark	silver	sprinkle	September	shook
sharp	sugar	squirrel	serve	wolf
smart	summer	travel	thirty	woman
start	wonder	turtle	worse	wool

A Reason For Spelling®

Dear Parent,

    We are about to begin the last spelling unit of the year containing only one lesson. A set of fifteen words will be studied next week. All the words will be reviewed the following week. Values based on the Scripture listed below will be taught.

Lesson 31

boot	group	shampoo
choose	loose	smooth
drew	moon	suit
flew	pool	truth
fruit	ruler	Tuesday

I Peter 1:2

A **Preview**

Write each word as your teacher says it.

Name _____

1. _____

2. _____

3. _____

4. _____

5. _____

6. _____

7. _____

8. _____

9. _____

10. _____

11. _____

12. _____

13. _____

14. _____

15. _____

Scripture

I Peter 1:2

Name _____

Write each word in the correct word shape boxes. Next, in the word shape boxes, color the letter or letters that spell the sound of /ü/ in each word.

1. boot

2. choose

3. drew

4. flew

5. fruit

6. group

7. loose

8. moon

9. pool

10. ruler

11. shampoo

12. smooth

13. suit

14. truth

15. Tuesday

C Hide and Seek

Place an **X** on a coin for each word you spell correctly.

D Other Word Forms

Using the words below, follow the instructions given by your teacher.

boots	fruits	pools	smoothness
choosing	grouped	ruled	suitable
chose	grouping	rules	suited
chosen	loosely	ruling	truthful
drawing	loosen	shampooed	truthfulness
drawn	looser	shampooing	
flies	loosest	smoothing	
flying	pooled	smoothly	

E Fun Ways to Spell

Initial the box of each activity you finish.

1.

Spell your words with puzzles.

3.

Spell your words in rhythm.

2.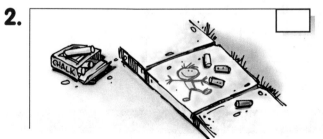

Spell your words with sidewalk chalk.

4.

Spell your words with play dough.

Complete the Word

Fill in the missing letters to complete each word in the puzzle.

1. even
2. suds to wash hair
3. free
4. heavenly body
5. select
6. swimming hole
7. high shoe
8. sketched
9. soared
10. day of the week
11. matched outfit
12. apple, peach
13. crowd
14. fact
15. yardstick

1. | o | o |
2. | | | | | o | o |
3. | o | o |
4. | o | o |
5. | o | o |
6. | o | o |
7. | o | o |
8. | e | w |
9. | e | w |
10. | u | e |
11. | u | i |
12. | u | i |
13. | o | u |
14. | u |
15. | u |

Word Bank

boot	flew	loose	ruler	suit
choose	fruit	moon	shampoo	truth
drew	group	pool	smooth	Tuesday

G Dictation

Name _____

Listen and write the missing words and punctuation.

1. _____ _____ _____ _____ _____ _____

   _____ _____ _____ _____

2. _____ _____ _____ _____

   gazed _____ _____ _____ _____ stars _____

3. _____ _____ _____ _____ fear _____

   _____ _____ _____ trust _____ _____

H Proofreading

If a word is misspelled, fill in the oval by that word. If all the words are spelled correctly, fill in the oval by **no mistake**.

1. ◯ boot
   ◯ chooz
   ◯ brook
   ◯ no mistake

2. ◯ drew
   ◯ bushes
   ◯ cookie
   ◯ no mistake

3. ◯ floo
   ◯ good-bye
   ◯ neighborhood
   ◯ no mistake

4. ◯ froot
   ◯ group
   ◯ notebook
   ◯ no mistake

5. ◯ pulley
   ◯ wolf
   ◯ loos
   ◯ no mistake

6. ◯ moon
   ◯ return
   ◯ needle
   ◯ no mistake

7. ◯ poole
   ◯ ruler
   ◯ shampoo
   ◯ no mistake

8. ◯ smooth
   ◯ siut
   ◯ wool
   ◯ no mistake

9. ◯ truth
   ◯ Tuezday
   ◯ woman
   ◯ no mistake

199

Join Christopher and his classmates at the Star Party. Move one space for each word you or your team spells correctly from this week's word list.

Remember: God has the power to free you from your fears!

J | **Journaling**

In your journal, write a paragraph about a time when you were afraid.

A Test-Editing

Name _____

If a word is spelled correctly, fill in the oval under **Correct**. If the word is misspelled, fill in the oval under **Incorrect**, and spell the word correctly on the blank.

	Correct	Incorrect	
1. boot	⬭	⬭	_____
2. chooz	⬭	⬭	_____
3. drue	⬭	⬭	_____
4. frute	⬭	⬭	_____
5. groop	⬭	⬭	_____
6. moon	⬭	⬭	_____
7. ruler	⬭	⬭	_____
8. shampoo	⬭	⬭	_____
9. smouth	⬭	⬭	_____
10. sute	⬭	⬭	_____
11. truth	⬭	⬭	_____
12. tuzday	⬭	⬭	_____
13. loos	⬭	⬭	_____
14. flue	⬭	⬭	_____
15. pool	⬭	⬭	_____

B Game

Go with Rachel to the hospital to visit her new baby brother and sister. Move one space for each word you or your team spells correctly.

Name _____

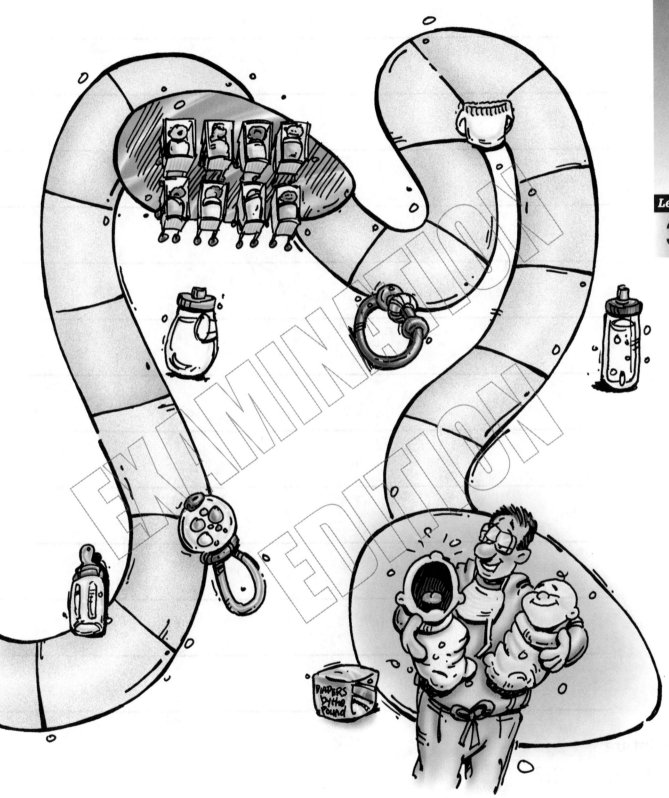

Remember: Be joyful and thankful before the Lord!

Write a story about what you think the baby shower for the Jacobson twins might be like.

_____

_____

_____

_____

_____

_____

_____

_____

_____

_____

_____

_____

Scripture

Colossians 2:7

D Proofing

Name _____

Use proofreader's marks to show the errors in the Baby Announcement below. Write the misspelled words correctly on the lines.

⬭ word is misspelled	ℒ take out word	☰ capitalize letter
⌄ comma is missing	⊙ period is missing	⋀ word or words missing

we have twins so small and swete,

They make our our family lighf complete!

We'll lern the joys that twins can bring,

We'll fill our home baby things-

Baby bottels, spoons and bibs,

fluffy blankets for for their cribs,

Dressing tabul, rocking chair,

Hats or ribbons their hair-

they will will bring us so much joy,

Our brand new babe girl and boy!

Names: Benjamin Joseph and Leah catherine jacobson

Date Date: may 23 1999

Weight: 6 lbs 13 oz. / 6 lbs. 12 oz

Parents: helen and David Jacobson

1. _____   3. _____   5. _____

2. _____   4. _____   6. _____

Find each of the bold words in the sentences below and circle them in the puzzle.

a	w	a	h	l	i	s	t	w	a	t	g	h
w	g	t	h	o	u	g	h	o	b	e	a	o
a	g	b	o	t	c	r	a	r	o	l	s	s
k	i	r	o	w	h	a	n	e	h	e	l	d
e	f	i	d	r	a	n	k	p	a	p	e	r
q	t	g	r	a	n	d	f	a	t	h	e	r
u	i	h	w	p	g	m	u	p	i	o	p	s
i	s	t	o	w	e	o	l	r	q	n	e	u
e	r	b	m	o	u	t	h	e	u	e	m	i
t	j	o	a	o	c	h	a	v	i	s	i	t
m	u	t	n	l	r	e	a	l	l	y	d	w
a	i	t	i	n	y	r	p	r	o	u	d	v
d	c	l	o	t	h	e	s	q	u	i	l	t
e	e	e	l	o	p	e	n	e	d	u	e	s

1. Mom made a **list** of things she would need for the baby.
2. We were eager to **visit** Mom in the hospital.
3. We called my **grandfather** and **grandmother** on the **telephone**.
4. Mom **held** a baby in her arms. It was **awake**.
5. The baby **opened** her **mouth** and gave a **loud** cry.
6. Father said it was time to **change** a diaper.
7. Benjamin was **asleep** even **though** Leah was not **quiet**.
8. Each baby **wore** a little **wool** **suit** with a **hood**.
9. The baby **clothes** looked so **tiny**.
10. A **woman** brought a **gift** in **really** pretty **paper**.
11. Grandma had **made** a **bright** **quilt** to **wrap** each baby in.
12. The babies woke up in the **middle** of the night.
13. Benjamin **drank** a **bottle** of **juice**.
14. We are **proud** of and **thankful** for our babies.

206

Spelling Is Fun!

This certificate is awarded to

_____

for practicing the following words, by doing terrific
spelling activities, and playing great spelling games!

Date _____

boot	group	shampoo
choose	loose	smooth
drew	moon	suit
flew	pool	truth
fruit	ruler	Tuesday

A Reason For SPELLING